MINDFUL EMOTIONAL EATING

Mindfulness Skills to Control
Cravings, Eat in Moderation
and Optimize Coping

BY PAVEL G. SOMOV, PhD

Copyright © 2015 by Pavel G. Somov
Published by
PESI Publishing and Media
PESI, Inc
3839 White Ave
Eau Claire, WI 54703

Cover Design: Amy Rubenzer
Layout Design: Amy Rubenzer
Edited By: Kayla Omtvedt

Printed in the United States of America

ISBN: 9781559570039

PESI
Publishing
& Media
www.pesipublishing.com

"Don't be fooled by the seeming contradiction in the title of *Mindful Emotional Eating*. The book makes the case to troubled eaters and their treaters that if we're going to turn to food when we're stressed or distressed, we best do it not with guilt, shame, self-hatred, or detachment from our bodies and their cravings, but with a keen mindfulness that will satisfy our appetites and foster emotional well-being."

—**Karen R. Koenig, LCSW, M.Ed.**, psychotherapist, eating coach, and and author of *Outsmarting Overeating*

"This wonderfully creative book teaches us that we don't need willpower to overcome our unruly eating habits, but mindfulness skill power. It shows that freedom doesn't come from stopping emotional eating, but when we learn how to eat emotionally in moderation, more effectively and without self-judgement or self-loafing. Pavel Somov has put together a fun mindfulness toolbox for not only healthcare professionals, but anyone who struggles with emotional eating."

—**Alexa Frey**, Co-Founder, The Mindfulness Project, (London, UK)

"Dr. Pavel Somov's newest book, *Mindful Emotional Eating*, offers individuals struggling with eating concerns a revolutionary guidebook for developing a satisfying, enjoyable relationship to food. The book challenges prevailing notions by de-pathologizing emotional eating and affirms that emotional eating is one among many ways that we can care for ourselves. His "humanistic harm reduction" approach helps people shift from demonizing emotional eating to affirming that we all eat for emotional reasons. The positive change we seek is from mindless to mindful moderate emotional eating. His mindful emotional eating (MEE) process is the antidote to the shame, blame, self-attacks and rebellious over-eating that characterize mindless emotional eating. MEE empathizes with people's need to self-soothe and empowers people to choose how they want to do it. His Jumpstart is filled with inspiring ideas and practical strategies for developing moderate emotional eating. Ultimately this book helps us become aware, self-compassionate and empowered with the confidence and skills to choose how to best care for ourselves in each moment. Quite a lot to get from one small book! I highly recommend it to practitioners and people with eating concerns."

—**Andrew Tatarsky, PhD,** leading expert in Integrative Harm Reduction Psychotherapy

About the Author

Pavel G. Somov, Ph.D., is author of 7 mindfulness-based books, including *Reinventing the Meal, Eating the Moment, Present Perfect, The Lotus Effect* and *Anger Management Jumpstart*. He is on the Advisory Board of the Mindfulness Project, (London, UK) and he regularly blogs and writes for PsychCentral. Dr. Somov lives, works, and meditates in Pittsburgh, PA.

Contents

Foreword

Pavel's *Mindful Emotional Eating* is a gem of a toolkit that will be invaluable both to individuals seeking a mindful eating self-help option and to practitioners looking to infuse more mindfulness into their work with clients distressed by emotional eating. The humanistic harm reduction approach is a breath of fresh air on a topic that is particularly difficult to address sanely in the current culture. Obesity has become a "hot" topic; it threatens the health of the next generation and will bankrupt our health care system if we cannot find a better way to come to terms with the inherent double bind society has created. Food is engineered to appeal directly to our biologically-based preferences for sugar and fat and food is more accessible than ever before. We are subjected to an overload of advertising with the messages: "Indulge yourself–you deserve it" and "More is better." A "tall" is the smallest option even available at Starbucks®. Marketers appear to believe that small or medium sounds so negative that only a fool would want such an option. If food portions are all "above average," our weight will also be above average.

Under the current circumstances, no knowledgeable person is surprised by the increase in obesity, but short of invoking a food police state, a viable solution remains elusive. Substantial long-term weight loss for those who are already obese requires nothing less than a lifestyle makeover that must be maintained forever, and only the most motivated individuals have been able to do this successfully. Many experts in the field have essentially given up on treating morbid obesity except for bariatric surgery that puts up physical roadblocks that slow down overeating. Hope for the future is pretty much invested in prevention and early intervention, especially in children where we may be able to moderate eating behaviors before our bodies are already compromised. This is where the current push for mindful eating comes into play and where Pavel's work has such an important role. Mindful eating can in fact take a person who is overeating and restore a more natural eating pattern that is less likely to contribute to weight gain even in our food-rich culture. However, I caution that expectations (of oneself or one's clients) must be realistic about weight loss. Mindful eating is a great tool but substantial weight loss requires a bit more. To get rid of the accumulated effects of overeating, some period of "subnormal eating" and/or high intensity exercise will be needed. Thus, obese individuals must understand that while mindful eating is great (and the best option available to avoid aversive deprivation states), it is not a magic bullet that will solve all their weight woes. On the other hand, for the mildly overweight and the not yet overweight, mindful eating is almost certainly their best option to establish a moderate eating pattern that is truly sustainable.

Pavel's 4-step program is mindful eating at its best. Pavel brings his extensive experience with mindfulness to the table. He puts a new frame around many of the cognitive-behavioral techniques that have been well established as helpful in normalizing eating and he fills in some of the empty spaces CBT hasn't successfully addressed. His approach feels both very familiar and quite new. Individuals trained to use CBT strategies will recognize many of the skills they already use (e.g. putting the fork down between bites) but the rationale for those strategies is a bit different and, at least to me, more compelling. The goal of all the strategies Pavel promotes is to keep one tuned in to the present moment so as to avoid slipping into the mindless eating that is a direct path to overeating. Most importantly, Pavel convincingly argues that all eating is emotional eating. This means there is no separate category of "emotional eating" that one needs to eliminate. This idea is helpful because it at least eliminates the self-judgment that fuels the maladaptive dieting cycle. What you need to do is remain mindful no matter why you are eating. While this is quite a difficult task since we are so inclined to do almost everything mindlessly, at least it is crystal clear what you need to do. Moreover, Pavel provides some creative new skills training to help you do that more successfully and feel much better about yourself in the process.

Pavel starts by addressing practitioners because he has found that "therapy" people are particularly likely to label emotional eating as "pathological" or at best, a "crutch" that they hope their client will soon be able to discard once they understand their feelings and learn better ways to cope with their feelings. Pavel turns this way of thinking on its head when he states unequivocally that "all eating is emotional eating". Obviously, one can't eliminate all eating so one can't eliminate emotional eating and that notion is now off the table.

Pavel and I are on the same page about "legalizing" emotional eating so I am delighted to see where he has taken the emotional eating debate. As he mentions, I have endorsed the idea of "effective emotional eating" for some time, but Pavel has taken this idea and pushed it a step further. While I have endorsed accepting emotional eating as a reasonable option when nothing else seemed viable (as long as one didn't eat to the point of uncomfortable fullness), my thinking was still stuck in the notion that other alternatives (i.e. non-food coping strategies) were preferable. I thought of eating for emotional reasons (rather than just to satisfy biological needs) as bound to happen but as an inherently risky business because when you start to eat for emotional reasons (either to celebrate or to self-soothe) it is so much harder to stay mindful and stop as soon as you get full. If you don't start because you are hungry, why would you stop when you are full? You'd be much more likely to keep eating until the food was gone, you felt better or you had eaten so much you really didn't want any more. That point, I contended was almost always far more calories that you needed so you were likely to end up feeling worse rather than better after an episode of emotional eating. While I still think that is true, Pavel puts a positive spin on ways to reduce that risk.

Pavel's label of *Mindful Emotional Eating* puts the spotlight squarely on the "how"- what skills does one need to achieve effective emotional eating? Pavel would say the skill is mindful eating and that goes for ALL eating, i.e. whether one is labeling it as emotional or not emotional. What Pavel has managed to do is help all of us get "unstuck" from the dichotomous thinking trap that there is eating to satisfy biological needs and eating to satisfy emotional needs. Many of us (especially me) thought that by shifting the focus from food type to the function that eating was serving (i.e. eat in response to hunger not in response to feelings and stop eating when full regardless of your feelings) we could eliminate the good food/bad food distinction that leads virtually everyone down a path of feeling deprived because eventually you want some "bad" foods. The shift away from food type and calorie counting to eating in response to appetite was a positive step. One is much less likely to feel deprived if you are allowed to all foods, just in moderation. However, reading Pavel I have come to believe that in some ways the focus just shifted so that eating in response to appetite cues was now the "good" way to eat and eating in response to emotions became the "bad" or at least the "less good" way to eat. The essence of mindfulness is "observing without judging" so mindfulness thinking will help us resist labeling any kind of eating as "bad" which frees us up to see more clearly about what we are thinking and feeling and to make behavioral choices based on our personal experience of reality.

I am excited to add Pavel's *Mindful Emotional Eating* to my work with clients and I challenge you to try it as well. Pavel has a knack for labeling strategies in an innovative way that helps one keep them in mind. I find myself thinking of taking an *mmm-ful* before I put a bite in my mouth, which is exactly the point. Whatever it takes, we must find ways to keep our thinking about eating very fresh to avoid lapsing into the void of mindless eating. I wish you well on a lifetime of mindful eating.

Linda W. Craighead, Ph.D.,
Professor of Psychology & Director of Clinical Training, Emory University,
author of *The Appetite Awareness Workbook*

Introduction

You don't need to completely eliminate emotional eating.
You can learn to use food more effectively to feel better occasionally
without relying on it to fix all your feelings. Deciding to have a treat
may be the most viable option you have in certain situations.

Linda Craighead, *The Appetite Awareness Workbook*

• • • • • • •

Here's a question that's on my clinical mind a lot: "What do my clients want and how do I help them get what they want?" This very question, as I see it, is at the core of humanistic harm reduction (HHR). When my client presents with concerns about "emotional eating," I ask myself the same question. When you get in the habit of asking yourself this question, the answer becomes rather self-evident. What my emotional eating clients want is obvious: They want to eat when they feel bad and they want to feel in control (both during and after emotional eating). But they have come to believe that eating to cope and feeling in control are somehow mutually exclusive. Not so! We can help our clients have exactly what they want. Yes, they can eat to cope and, yes, they can feel in control (both during and after the emotional eating episode). How? With the help of mindful emotional eating (MEE). Mindful emotional eating satisfies two self-regulation fantasies: To eat and to feel in control. Mindful emotional eating allows your client to pursue change without sacrificing what they want. To clarify, this book is not about emotional eating. It's about mindful emotional eating. The book is not about how to stop emotional eating but about how to eat emotionally in moderation, more effectively, and without self-judgment and self-loathing.

MEE: Enabling Optimal Self-Care

Mindful Emotional Eating (MEE) has been nearly a taboo both in self-help and clinical literature on emotional eating. I first wrote about mindful emotional eating in Eating the Moment (New Harbinger, 2008) and have had a chance to pilot this material clinically in my practice and through a series of workshops for mental health professionals. My experience reveals that while the idea of mindful emotional eating makes a lot of sense to my clients, surprisingly, the mental health professionals often bristle with objections, barricading behind the all-or-nothing belief that any emotional eating is self-destructive and to be avoided at all costs. These clinicians say that they are afraid to "enable" their clients. By that they mean that they don't want to "join in" or "to collude" in the "clearly self-destructive" behavior of emotional eating. Not so: emotional eating is not self-destructive. Emotional eating is self-care. Dare to "enable" your client's self-care.

A humanistic clinician operates on the following two assumptions:

- He/she takes it as a given that we are always pursuing wellbeing; I call this "motivational innocence."
- He/she takes it as a given that we are always doing our coping best (even if it doesn't seem so to an uninformed mind of an observer). I call this "ordinary perfection."

With this in mind, a humanistic clinician doesn't believe in self-destructive behavior. All behavior is seen as a motivationally innocent attempt at self-regulation, i.e. as homeostatic. A humanistic clinician's role is not to uninstall the coping that already works somewhat but to help upgrade clients' coping software, to help clients optimize their coping.

Self-destructiveness is a psychological myth. The method proposed in this program is a direct challenge to the all-too-common clinical position that pathologizes emotional eating and offers emotional eaters nothing more than a psychological diet of abstinence from emotional eating. More than ever before, I am convinced that as a culture and a civilization we have to begin to re-integrate emotional eating back into our eating lives. It is high time that we take emotional eating out of the closet of self-care and "legalize" it – psychologically, clinically, and culturally.

Jumpstart: Getting Unstuck

In thinking about how we, as an eating culture, conceptualize emotional eating I envision a broken down family van on the side of the road. Inside of it is the back-and-forth bickering between parents and children, between superegos and ids – with the former telling the latter to "Stop it." and the latter saying to the former "But I wanna."

You, the clinical reader, and you, the client, know exactly what you want. We all have been stuck like this before, when stressed or overwhelmed. We all have gotten past a challenging moment with a pacifier of food in our mouth. And that didn't kill us, did it? We've all gotten unstuck with a scoop of ice cream or a few squares of a chocolate bar or a serving or two of mashed potatoes. Yes, we've all had this kind of emotional eating in moderation. But we've all also overdone it too. I am yet to meet someone who hasn't yet binged once. We all have gotten stuck in mindless emotional overeating (on a Sunday night before the work week, after a failed date, etc.) and couldn't get unstuck until we stuffed ourselves. It was in those kinds of moments that we stopped trusting ourselves and really got stuck, got stuck in the fantasy of abstinence, in the dream of "never doing this again."

You or your client don't really need a tow truck. You need a jumpstart – a bit of craving control know-how, some self-acceptance, some awareness and someone to show some clinical faith in your ability to indulge in moderation.

It's Time for a Paradigm Shift

The clinical field of eating disorders has been stuck in a perfectionistic, purist, puritanical mindset on the issue of emotional eating: "Emotional eating is bad. We must end it. It's self-destructive." We have been fussing around this issue, trying to get it out of the ditch of our unrealistic expectations, trying to fix it every which way but mostly to no avail. Other psychological and behavioral issues, other bodies of clinical and self-help literature have long passed us by on this freeway to wellbeing and treatment outcomes. Even the field of addiction, from which we, the field of emotional eating, have borrowed the misguided paradigm of abstinence, has long moved on by, evolving from its own all-or-nothing dogma to a more humanistic, moderation-focused discourse. But we, the emotional eaters and our clinical entourage, are still in the ditch, by the side of the road, sitting on the empty tires of not allowing ourselves to feed our chronic emptiness, drained from the years of stoic self-denial and ever unwilling to trust ourselves to find balanced self-care.

We know what we want: We want to be able to eat to cope, to eat for emotional reasons – now and then. We know why we want that, because it feels intuitive and because it works – it does help us feel better and does help us get unstuck emotionally in a pinch. We just don't know how to use this strategy without abusing it and we don't have the cultural permission to use it without feeling like we are doing something wrong. We are waiting for someone to let us, to trust us, to show faith in our ability to know moderation, to help us learn how to do it without overdoing it. We are in a dire need for a jumpstart, for a paradigm-shift, for a pattern-break, for something new to try. This someone will have to be you, yourself – you, the clinician, and you, the emotional overeater.

This book is that jumpstart. What is a jumpstart? A jumpstart, whether it's of the roadside-assistance kind or the clinical kind along the road of life, brings energy to an impasse. It helps you get unstuck and gets you going again. The jumpstart that you'll find in this book is a brief, problem-focused intervention to help you break through a clinical impasse (see Part I). I won't keep you tied down on the side of the road for too long: Four sessions and some juice for your clinical batteries, and you'll be back on the road in no time. The rest (Part II) is optional.

But before you move on, let me be crystal clear: The goal of this program is nothing less than to learn to leverage more coping per calorie, to help you and/or your clients to learn to become effective, mindful emotional eaters, and to finally re-integrate emotional eating back into our inevitably emotional lives – with unconditional self-acceptance instead of that toxic heartburn of shame and guilt that has been eating at us for years whenever we would turn to food for some self-directed TLC.

Overview: Short-Term and Long-Term Management of Emotional Eating

There are two main parts to this book: Part I deals with short-term management of emotional overeating and Part II takes a longer clinical perspective on working with the issue. Whereas Part I could be conceptualized as a tool-belt, Part II is a toolbox. Part I is a 4-session long, rapid-fire, humanistic, experiential, mindfulness-powered clinical protocol for helping a mindless emotional eater become a mindful emotional eater. Part I consists of a psycho-educational component that is designed to help your client shift from self-loathing to self-acceptance. The idea here is to help your client rethink emotional eating so as to rethink what to do about emotional eating. The rest of Part I has to do with highly practical, no-nonsense craving control training, emotional self-regulation training and training in the so-called choice awareness – an awareness-building and habit-modification change-hygiene factor. The meaning of all this will become clear as you read on. Part I is "third wave" psychology – it is a primarily post-cognitive, highly experiential, mindfulness-powered approach to working with this population.

In Part I, you will learn the architecture of a mindful emotional eating meal, which is:

Course 1: Emptying Your Mind
Course 2: Waking Up Your Mind
Course 3: Keeping Your Mind Awake
Course 4: Never Minding Your Mind/Letting Your Mind

There is another way to express this mindful emotional eating algorithm through a metaphor of "connection":

Course 1: Connecting to Your Body
   (through relaxation)
Course 2: Connecting to Your Mind
   (through choice awareness & pattern breaks)
Course 3: Connecting to Reality/World-at-Large
   (through process-focused mindful eating)
Course 4: Reconnecting to Your Bodymind
   (through satiety/fullness awareness)

Part II offers a series of long-term interventions designed to help your client make a kind of existential correction from self-loathing and self-doubt to effective self-care and unconditional self-acceptance. Furthermore, Part II offers you and your clients an opportunity to develop a self-referenced sense of identity which serves to immunize the mind against various ego wounds that might provoke a relapse into mindless emotional eating. Part II ends with a brief review of the Eastern know-how of emptying your illusory sense of self so as to feel existentially full.

Part III is devoted to emotion-specific applications of MEE. Consider these to be an advanced form of mindful emotional eating only to be tried when the basics are behaviorally and attitudinally well in place. In closing, I call on you, the reader, to open your mind; you might as well since you already opened this book. I'll see you on the other end of this process of clinical self-improvement.

Part I: Short Term MEE

—✢—

Chapter 1 | Opening the Mind
(Psychodydactics)

One should speak only that word by which one would not
torment oneself nor harm others. That word is indeed well spoken.
The Noble Eightfold Path

Don't let them fool ya. Or even try to school ya.
Oh no! We've got a mind of our own.
Bob Marley

Instead of pushing away your urge to eat/binge, you must give yourself
permission to eat the type of food you really want. You can eat a small
amount, a moderate amount or even a substantial amount. You just don't
give yourself the permission to get uncomfortably full or stuffed. It sounds too
simple but it works. All you have to do is be willing to give yourself conscious
permission. That conscious decision undermines any sense of loss of control.
Linda Craighead, *The Appetite Awareness Workbook*

• • • • • • •

Mindful Emotional Eating is 4 sessions long – the first session is psychodydactic (psycho-educational); the rest is experiential skills-training. In session 1 your job as a clinician is to open your client's mind to a different way of thinking about emotional eating. If you are a self-help reader, then your job is to open your own mind... or let me open it with the help of this chapter.

Reframing the Problem to Reframe the Solution

The first step doesn't have to be the hardest but it does call for an open mind and a good bit of courage to let go of what you've come to believe – both as a clinician and a client. Emotional eating has been misunderstood and unnecessarily demonized. The first business of Mindful Emotional Eating is to de-pathologize and to normalize emotional eating. We, as clinicians, will accomplish this by reframing the problem of emotional eating and by rethinking the solution to it. Thus, the first session is necessarily psycho-educational (psychodydactic) in format and humanistic in tone. But just because it is largely informational in nature, the first session doesn't have to be boring or dry. It can be Socratic and interactive.

Clinical Samma Vacca

Samma vacca (which means "right speech") is one of the eight ways of being virtuous on the path to enlightenment in Buddhist psychology. Right speech is non-divisive. What that means is that when you talk your speech works to integrate reality rather than fragment it. The principle of non-divisive speech is essential in helping frame the vector of the recovery narrative.

How we talk about any given issue in treatment makes all the difference. When we approach emotional eating from the standpoint of abstinence we are dividing all eating into good and bad and, in so doing, we are dividing and fragmenting our clients into "being good" (when they just eat) and "being bad" (when they eat to cope). When, however, we approach the issue of emotional eating from the standpoint of humanistic harm reduction, all eating – be it purely metabolic or explicitly emotional – is now seen as belonging to one and the same unifying continuum of pursuing wellbeing.

With this mind, the language of humanistic harm reduction seems to be exactly the right clinical speech whereas the all-or-nothing language of the abstinence models strikes me as divisive, outdated, and arguably, psychologically toxic. I realize that it is not very samma vacca of me to say so. But one has to draw a line of division somewhere. And that's where this line is for me.

The Initial Clinical Thrust

The initial thrust of our intervention is an unapologetic debunking of the psychologically toxic dogma about emotional eating. Your clients come to you feeling ashamed about their emotional eating. They feel that they have been self-destructive. Nothing is further from the truth. As a clinician, you should be prepared to rigorously yet matter-of-factly challenge your client's view of emotional eating as "being bad" or "being self-destructive." In sum, the first intervention of MEE involves the following three educational and therapeutic tasks:

- **Humanistic Normalization**

    Key ideas: *"Emotional eating is a legitimate form of self-soothing and coping"* and *"Emotional eating is inevitable."*

- **Humanistic Reframing of the Problem**

    Key ideas: *"Emotional eating is not a problem, emotional over-eating is a problem"* and *"Emotional eating is not a problem, mindless emotional over-eating is a problem."*

- **Harm Reduction Goal Setting**

    Key ideas: *"What is needed is a shift from willpower to skillpower"* and *"What is needed is a shift from abstinence to moderation, from mindless emotional over-eating to mindful, effective and skillful emotional eating in moderation."*

If you are stranded by the roadside in the middle of the rain, you want your AAA® rescuer to have an upbeat, energetic, problem-solving attitude, right? As a clinician who is trying to jumpstart a long-standing coping impasse, you'd do well to have some thrust to your tone as you challenge the prevailing cultural and clinical dogma about emotional eating. But beware: Thrust isn't zeal; thrust is the energy of conviction.

This might or might not be your style, but see if you can allow yourself to sound a bit appalled by the notion that emotional eating is somehow self-destructive. No, you don't need to stomp your feet or yell out "Preposterous!" But a smidgen of indignation *on your client's behalf* would certainly help the rapport. As a result, your client is likely to feel safe with you. To their surprise they begin to suspect that you feel that they have simply been taking care of themselves the best way they know how. And they will feel that you are unambiguously on their side. While they don't yet understand exactly where you are coming from, they will however intuitively feel that you are coming from a place of acceptance, compassion and moderation. And that will feel good to them. And what feels good to a client bodes well for rapport and treatment compliance, at least initially.

Psychodydactic Bombardment

How about that for an opening volley? Now let me bombard you with a bunch of various points and angles so that we can get on the same page. I'll throw at you all I can, like I do with my clients. Everything one can think of and maybe even the kitchen sink too. What follows is a pitch, a clinical sales pitch. I am selling you an idea and I am selling you how to sell it. Read through this chapter, take notes, and figure out your own clinical sales pitch. But beware:

what is being sold here is a paradigm breaker to many. So prepare to feel like a Prius salesman in the wild gas guzzling 1990s. And bear with me if I repeat myself here and there: Any effective sales pitch has an element of hypnotic circularity. Now, when I say "clinical sales pitch," I don't mean to suggest that you down an energy drink and do a "We buy any car." hip hop dance. I am talking about you offering a number of psychoeducational points to make. That's it; nothing more hard-boiled than that.

Sales Pitch Angle 1:
Emotional Eating is Inevitable

Here are 10 ways to clinically pitch the idea of mindful emotional eating. These clinical sales pitches are intended to de-pathologize and to normalize emotional eating. As we go on, we will also tackle any related objections as they might naturally arise. So, let's begin.

All eating is emotional because we are emotional creatures. Put differently, emotional eating is inevitable because we are inevitably emotional. Feeling down is an emotional state but so is feeling calm. And so is feeling joyful. Whether you are eating to cope or eating to celebrate, whether you are eating to numb out or to spice things up, your eating is inevitably emotional.

The only unemotional eating is mindless eating. And mindless eating, for all intents and purposes, is not really eating but reflexive, robotic, conditioned hand-to-mouth feeding behavior. Mechanical and mindless intake of food is no more eating than pumping some nutritive sludge through a feeding tube in the side of your body is eating. Feeding isn't eating.

Sales Pitch Angle 2:
Mindful Eating is Emotional Eating

To eat mindfully is to savor. To savor is to notice pleasure. To notice pleasure is to notice emotion. Conclusion: Mindful eating is emotional eating. Put differently, mindful eating is necessarily and inevitably emotional. If you are eating without any emotion, then you are either rushing to down some kind of Soylent Green® or you are eating mindlessly. But, as we have just established, mindless eating isn't really eating. Mindless eating is a mechanical intake of food. Mindless eating is just feeding. My point is this: all true eating is mindful eating and all truly mindful eating is emotional because it involves a savoring of pleasure which is to say that it involves emotionality. A person that tells you that you shouldn't engage in emotional eating is a self-unaware hypocrite. You leave and they themselves go shopping – not for some tasteless Soylent Green but for something yummy, for something to enjoy. Their core motivation behind eating is same as yours – to enjoy themselves through eating.

Objections Are Welcome: Say Your Piece

"But wait a second, Pavel." you might exclaim in objection, "You've just up and changed what is usually meant by emotional eating. Not fair." Indeed, I have. Guilty as charged but not feeling guilty. It's time we redefine emotional eating. Emotional eating, as most of your clients have come learn, is still widely seen as escapist and self-destructive. Most of your clients will unambiguously define emotional eating as a problem and define the solution to it as figuring out a way to never do it again. With this kind of perfectionistic rigid tenacity they de-humanize what is so fundamentally human – the idea of using food to feel better. Like some self-exiled pariahs your clients deny themselves the basic pleasure of eating while the rest of us are going wild with our culturally sanctioned Superball®-scale merry-eating. As a clinician, your job here is to keep these pitiful lemmings of abstinence from trying to leave the world of eating pleasure for good. (Now, when I say "pitiful lemmings of abstinence" to you in this text I mean it in a most heartfelt sense, there is no scorn here, just a provocative style to keep the task of writing interesting to myself and to keep the task of reading interesting to you. So give me a benefit of the doubt here, will ya?) You and your client now stand to daringly and radically rethink the problem and the solution to it. The challenge is nothing less than to jumpstart a cultural and clinical impasse in our relationship to this universal dimension of eating. The goal is to re-integrate emotional eating back into the repertoire of existential vibrant living. The goal, in sum, is to shift from mindless emotional overeating to mindful emotional eating in moderation.

Of Course, It's Not Easy

The task isn't easy: We, you and I, dear reader, are swimming upstream, against the long-standing currents of cultural demonization of emotional eating. To my knowledge of the relevant literature, there has been only one clinical voice that has been sounding a similar note of acceptance – a voice of Linda Craighead whose *Appetite Awareness Training* program includes training in Effective Emotional Eating (EEE). So, kudos to her, it took clinical courage and much humanistic savvy to break away from what is, in effect, emotional eating abstinence camp, or, as I jokingly call them, the "Triple-Es" – the "emotional eating enders." These "Triple-Es" are a legion, so let us take a quick farewell look at that all-or-nothing camp before we start talking about how to find a healthy, humanistic middle ground.

Watch Out for the Emotional Eating Enders

The history of emotional eating literature is best seen through the abstinence/harm-reduction lens. Just like the temperance movement of the yester year, the emotional eating abstinence camp is a bit on the moralizing and puritanical side. Emotional eating is seen as an enemy, a behavior to end altogether, as flat-out self-destruction. Abstinence-minded folks are great at catastrophizing and predicting an end of the world should you lapse or, God forbid, relapse. The advice from the "enders" spans the gamut – from simplistic (à la Nancy Reagan's "Say 'No' to Drugs.") to more clinically savvy – craving control and alternative coping. But the entire abstinence camp is united on one key point: Emotional eating has to be overcome. This perfectionistic, purist, puritanical zeal is clinically counterproductive. Clients and self-help readers are effectively set up for relapse dynamics (because of Marlattian "abstinence violation effects"). In a strange bit of justice, the "Say 'No' to Emotional Eating." authors are themselves locked into their own life-long hypocrisy battles (since I am sure that even the most devout "enders" now and then still eat to just indulge, for pleasure, when not hungry). Beware of extremes.

Sales Pitch Angle 3:
Emotional Eating Abstinence
Mentality is Diet Mentality is Mentality of Self-Denial

Curiously many of these emotional eating enders have no problem appreciating that diets do not work, that open-ended once-and-for-all abstinence from this or that is a lousy platform for sustainable change. Most of these authors and clinical thinkers would have no qualms about telling you to ditch your diet. And yet they'd stubbornly stand by their emotional eating abstinence position. But the two are the same in principle. Abstinence from emotional eating does not work for the exact same reason that diets don't work. "What's that reason?" you ask. Abstinence is that reason. Stoic, all-or-nothing, self-denying solutions don't last – be it about what you eat or why you eat. Understand: The advice to end emotional eating is a motivational diet, a diet that bans one of the basic motives behind eating. You are being told – in no uncertain terms – to never cope by eating. That's just unrealistic, idealistic bunk. You'll see why in a moment.

Dare to Repeat: "Emotional Eating is Inevitable"

Dare to repeat to your client: "Emotional eating isn't the problem, it's emotional overeating and mindless emotional eating that are the problem." Repeat: "Emotional eating is simply inevitable." The simple, humanistic harm reduction proposal is: "There is no need to eliminate emotional eating; instead we need to learn to use it in moderation with the help of mindfulness." Dare to repeat this MEE party line to your client.

✻

Sales Pitch Angle 4:
Pleasure is Mind-Business

Whether we eat or overeat, whether we eat when hungry or when mindlessly triggered (by any number of environmental stimuli that are designed to pull the strings of our appetite), whether we eat mindfully or mindlessly, one thing is clear: we only eat what we like. In other words, we all eat for taste. Indeed, when we shop we buy only what we like and want to eat. To like and to want are emotional reasons. Even the most health-conscious of us guide their food selections on the basis of taste. How something tastes is a hedonic consideration, i.e. a fundamentally emotional consideration.

Let's face it: your body doesn't give a hoot about taste, as long as food isn't rotten. Taste is mind-business. Bottom-line is all of us, mindful-eating writers, mindless-eating readers, health nuts and foodies – all of us accept the premise of eating pleasure. Even Soylent Green comes in more than one flavor. This premise of eating pleasure makes all emotional eating inevitable. So, stop beating yourself up for wanting to cope by eating. The reason why eating works as coping is because eating is emotionally pleasurable. So, let us once and for all bury this behaviorally unrealistic goal of entirely eliminating emotional eating. You have been eating for pleasure and you will continue to eat for pleasure, i.e. for emotional reasons unless, of course, you are into moralizing, stoic, self-punishment, in which case feel free to switch from pasta to boiled shoe laces.

Once again, the key point is this: "The problem isn't emotional eating. The problem can't be emotional eating because emotional eating is inevitable. And that which is inevitable is normal. The problem is mindless emotional eating which leads to emotional over-eating. And this problem can be solved: Mindless emotional eating can be made mindful." Starting to sound pretty familiar? Good.

⋰ᗱ

Sales Pitch Angle 5:
Emotional Eating Is Coping

Here's another pitch angle. This one is a clinical must. This one fundamentally and forcefully de-pathologizes and normalizes emotional eating. Your client will surely appreciate the validation contained herein. Your client is starved for having someone finally see where they are coming from. So, here it is.

Aside from normally hedonistic emotional eating that we all engage in, day in and day out, some of us eat to cope, i.e. not just for emotional pleasure but to reduce emotional distress. But eating for pleasure or eating to reduce distress are two sides of the same coin. They are essentially the same. And yet our dichotomous minds (not without some help from self-help authors) divide this indivisible coin in half. This, of course, creates the confusing twilight of hypocrisy. On one hand, we are encouraged to slow down and savor the food we eat – i.e. to enjoy it (which is a form of emotional eating since all pleasure is mind-business). On the other hand, we are told to never eat for emotional reasons. If this sounds like nonsense, it's because it is. Get this: Any pursuit of wellbeing is simultaneously a reduction of distress and a pursuit of pleasure. The only reason why we pursue stress reduction is because less stress is more pleasurable than more stress. Thus, a pursuit of an emotional plus is an avoidance of an emotional minus and an avoidance of an emotional minus is a pursuit of an emotional plus. Help your client collapse this semantic duality to see the innocent oneness of their pursuit of wellbeing.

Somehow we are encouraged to pursue the emotional plus through eating but are discouraged from avoiding the emotional minus through eating. We have come to demonize exactly half the coin of emotional eating. Help your client see that emotional eating with the explicit goal of alleviating emotional distress – motivationally – is a form of self-care and, as such, it needs to be legitimized and welcomed as an attempt at emotional self-regulation.

Sell this point to your client by offering a basic scenario:

> *"Say it's late at night and you feel stressed. Too late to exercise and you haven't yet figured out how to meditate effectively enough to deal with stress. So you sit down to eat. Why? Because you know it'll help and you just want to do something that works and go to sleep because life isn't gonna wait for you to catch up. Dare to see this as a step towards self-care. And stop comparing yourself to others. In any comparison between you*

and not-you, you will only find a difference. Just because someone else would/could cope differently with, say, exercise or meditation or support, it doesn't mean that right at this very moment you can. If you could have more resources at this very moment, if you could be right now psychologically-healthier than you are, you wouldn't be you, but you are you, not some theoretical you or abstract you, not the you the way you used to be, not the you you would like to be, but this here-and-now/real-time you, doing your best with what you got. Dare to see your motive and to accept your best effort even if it sucks in comparison to some unrealistic ideal."

Sales Pitch Angle 6:
Any Coping is Better than None

A humanistic clinician celebrates any coping, any self-care moment, however theoretically imperfect it might be. Dare to say the following to your clients in this regard:

"I know you are doing your best, which is good enough for me as your therapist, and I hope it can eventually feel like it's good enough for you too. God only knows what your life would have been like if you didn't have this powerful coping tool of emotional eating. Sure, you might have gained some weight. Sure, you might have even jeopardized your physical health somewhat. But, guess what. You made it. You survived. You stayed afloat. And coping by eating was the life raft you needed. This was creative coping. Congratulations to you. And, oh yeah, on that point of jeopardizing your health: You have more than one kind of health. Physical health matters. No doubt. But so does emotional health. You took care of your emotional wellbeing with the help of emotional eating. Who knows where you would have been emotionally if it hadn't been for these moments of eating self-care? What good would it have been to you if you had taken care of yourself physically while getting progressively worse emotionally? These emotional eating episodes you blame yourself for and feel ashamed about — there is a good chance you might have spared yourself a depressive stupor or two, maybe even saved your life. Same goes for any binges you might have had. Bottom line is you have nothing to feel ashamed about. Instead, you have something to celebrate. You survived, you are here, you are finally at a place where you are ready to update your coping software, to make better, smarter, more effective use of emotional eating. That's great news. Congrats."

No, you don't have to be that enthusiastic. But that is the angle of the pitch, the vector of this clinical thrust. And, when you can, recap the overall idea even if you have to repeat yourself:

> *"To sum up, before we continue, emotional eating isn't about self-destruction but about self-care (which is good news) and emotional eating, as a form of coping, can be fine-tuned (which is even better news)."*

All Coping Is Temporary

A common but naïve counterargument to the view of emotional eating as a form of coping is that it "only provides temporary relief." Here's how you tackle this little speed bump, this little abstinence pot hole of all-or-nothing thinking.

> *"All coping is temporary. All coping is tactical. Just because a Tylenol® doesn't last your whole life doesn't mean we shouldn't take it when we have a headache. By the same token, just because eating to cope doesn't solve the problem of chronic stress for good, it doesn't mean that we should deny ourselves an occasional coping short-cut by having a cookie or a piece of chocolate at the end of an exhausting day. Furthermore, what coping isn't temporary? Say, instead of coping by eating you did some yoga or spent half an hour in meditation or talked to a friend. The chances are that neither of these coping strategies would once and for all solve the issues that you are trying to cope with. Life is like that: it's full of long-term, chronic problems that resist simple, on-the-spot solutions. We can't always solve a given challenge of living in one fell swoop. That's where coping comes in — it buys time, allows us to survive, to stay afloat, to get by while we keep searching for a more permanent solution to a chronic problem. In sum, to say that emotional eating provides only short-lasting relief is to misunderstand the entire concept of coping. All coping is fundamentally short-term."*

Sales Pitch Angle 7:
Emotional Eating Works

Tell your client: "Before we talk about how to fine-tune emotional eating, let's pause to appreciate why it's so appealing as a coping strategy." This part of the clinical sales pitch is empowering and not to be overlooked. This particular pitch angle is like a cluster bomb — it kills not two, not three, not five birds at a time but just about the entire flock of anti-emotional eating objections.

Fire off these points with psychoeducational matter-of-factness and take any questions as they arise.

Pacifier = Oral Coping: From day one, feeding has been a default parenting intervention and the pacifier has been our first coping tool. Oral coping is power-coping which is why we all do it.

Feeding = Caring: Most cultures equate feeding with caring and even love. So then, why is it ok to show love and appreciation for others by feeding them but it is not ok to show self-love and self-care by feeding yourself? Of course, it is ok – we deserve this kind of love and this kind of care just as much as those that we ourselves love and care for.

Meal-time = Family-time = Support-time: We've been culturally conditioning ourselves for years to see dinner time as family time, to see eating together as a time of togetherness, as an opportunity for social relating and belonging, as a means to emotional well-being. So, then why do we have to deny ourselves the fruits of this kind of conditioning? Just because we overeat? Wouldn't that be tantamount to throwing the baby of eating out with the bathwater of mindless overeating? I say: Keep the conditioning, keep the power of habit, keep all of these emotionally stabilizing connotations of food and eating, and find a better, smarter, more effective way to get more coping out of less eating.

Eating = Grounding = Centering = Reality Check: Eating is a ritual. Rituals offer the comfort of predictability. Eating is also a sensation-rich, unambiguously physical activity – there is nothing abstract about it. And this sensory clarity of eating serves as a powerful reality check – it awakens us to what is, to the here-and-now moment of our life, cutting off the past and nailing us down to the present. At a time of uncertainty or confusion, eating behavior centers a suffering mind by providing it a kind of corridor of certainty. When we sit down to eat, we feel like we know what's next. And we do; eating is as familiar as gravity which is why it grounds us.

Eating = Relaxing: From the physiological perspective, a choice to eat is a choice to relax. Eating can be seen as a direct intuitive attempt to switch on the parasympathetic branch of the autonomic nervous system (PNS) which is associated with relaxation and rest. Sure, we can light up the candle of relaxation. And yes, we can orchestrate a kumbaya moment of social support. But all of that takes a good bit of effort. And sometimes we are too fried, too starved, and too desperate to cope to wait. So, why not flick on the simple light switch of PNS relaxation, particularly if it's on a dimmer of moderation?

Another Objection to Tackle:
"Emotional Eating is Mind-Gain at Body-Cost"

When presented with the reframe that emotional eating is a form of self-care, the following objection tends to come up: "Emotional eating might be good for the mind but it's not so good for the body. Emotional eating is a kind of self-care that takes care of the mind at the cost to the body." Of course, it does. But is that really atypical? We take care of our minds at the expense of the body all the time without giving it a second thought. You want ice cream and you go out for a drive to your local convenience store to get some, not at all worrying that people die in droves every year driving around in their cars. Or take any extreme sport for example: You go skiing or rock-climbing – for mind's fun – at the possibly catastrophic expense to your body, ranging from broken bones to paralysis to death. Or, you decide you want that 26.2 bumper sticker and you sign up to run a marathon just to boost your ego, to feel accomplished, while knowing all along that it is probably not all that great for your knees. Right? Right. Heck, forget the extreme sports. Take sex, for example. Sex – on a physiological level – is a pretty violent process. Heart rate goes up. Right? Right. So, should you then get permission from your PCP every time? Of course not. We place the wellbeing of the mind ahead of the wellbeing of the body all the time. So, let us not be hypocritically preachy about emotional eating.

We aren't the bodies we live in. We are the minds, the thinking, feeling, sensing neurons that drive around in these fleshy RVs. So, body is mind's money, mind's way to get by. And that's why mind is throwing it around. But mind doesn't have to spend indiscriminately, which is the point of this writing. You can learn to both take care of your mind with emotional eating and not overpay with your body. How? Once again by making your emotional eating more mindful, i.e. by leveraging more coping per calorie.

—✺—

Sales Pitch Angle 8:
"Leveraging More Coping Per Calorie"

This is my favorite angle, a logical power-punch, particularly well-suited for that obsessive, intellectualized mind that eats up logical argumentation. Check it out.

All coping can be viewed as a cost-to-benefit ratio: you give something up (say, time when you sit down to meditate) in order to get something (say, peace of mind). Same with emotional eating as a coping strategy: You reduce distress at a possible weight gain, a change of mind at a possible expense to body. The idea behind mindful emotional eating is to leverage more coping per calorie, i.e. to make emotional eating more effective. That's the goal: Not to quit emotional eating altogether (because that's just plain unrealistic) but to make emotional eating more effective, to learn to get more out of it on fewer calories. How? By making it more mindful. Case closed.

Not an All-or-Nothing Matter

When you are pitching hard there is a risk of pitching over. So, somewhere towards the mid-point of your clinical sales pitch you need to pull back a bit and sound the bell of moderation. It helps to preempt a misunderstanding when you can. Which one? The misunderstanding that you are saying that a client should engage in emotional eating. Of course not. You are not encouraging emotional eating. You are not being clinically permissive; you are not saying that the client should take it easy. You are just saying that sometimes the client must take it easy because they have to. Here's how you can clarify where you are coming from:

> *"Don't get me wrong. Of course, you don't have to always cope by eating and only by eating. If you can cope without eating, then, of course, do. But if you can't, consider optimizing your emotional eating coping. Or run the risk of self-denial that, as you have probably figured out, is an extreme that boomerangs with emotional over-eating. Your coping is only as steady as the coping paradigm you stand on. For years, you've been hearing from self-help authors and your therapists to stay away from such absolutizing words as "always" or "never." Time to take self-help extremism out of self-help. Next time you hear or read something along the lines that you should never, ever eat to cope, that you should always avoid emotional eating, think Middle Way, think Moderation."*

Sales Pitch Angle 9:
Invoke the Consensus

It helps to invoke the consensus, in particular, when one exists. Throughout the years I have been very impressed with the work of Dr. Linda Craighead, a clinician and a self-help author who too is shifting the paradigm of emotional eating towards a position of balanced moderation. Here's a sample of her provocative clarity about what she herself calls Effective Emotional Eating (EEE):

"Eating for emotional reasons is viewed as an acceptable coping strategy provided that you are able to stop at moderate fullness and that you don't use this strategy all the time."

"When nonfood alternatives are not easily available or are not working for you, you are encouraged to make a conscious decision to allow yourself self-soothing eating."

Agreed: The golden age of non-perfectionistic self-care, in general, and non-judgmental attitudes about emotional eating, in particular, is finally upon us.

Sales Pitch Angle 10:
Self-Acceptance = Compassion

Having pulled back a bit to a position of moderation, it's time to floor it to get over the remaining hump of self-rejection. The sales pitch angle here is that of self-acceptance. The goal is to help your emotional eating client see the big picture of Mindful Emotional Eating retraining. MEE is not just about eating, it's also about establishing a healthy relationship with yourself. So, here's the verbiage to borrow from.

> *"Is compassion an important value in your life? [Most clients will nod] You see, compassion begins as self-acceptance. You might have not thought of it this way but it does. Let me explain. It is only when we are able to own and accept our own coping that we begin to develop a sense of compassion for others' strife. Emotional eating is a powerful physiological short-cut and an intuitive coping choice. As an eating civilization, we have to own this, we have to normalize it, we have to de-demonize it, we have to psychologically "legalize" it and, in accordance with humanistic principle of harm reduction psychology, we have to help each other make it more mindful, with compassion and without judgment."*

Another Objection: "But Isn't This Enabling?"

Are we enabling your client with all of this talk of mindful emotional eating? I hope so. Wouldn't it be nice to en-*able* your client's ability to cope without being perfectionistic about their coping choices? Wouldn't it be nice to en-able your client's ability to cope with compassion for their own coping choices? Wouldn't it be nice to en-able your client's ability to cope with a sense of moderation and balance? Of course, it would.

You see, the word "enabling" has gotten an unnecessarily bad reputation. The verb to enable is a good, empowering verb. It means to leverage ability and to endow a capacity. The process of enabling in and of itself is not a problem, it's what we enable that may be problematic. We are not enabling your client to overeat. We are trying to enable your client to eat in moderation and to cope effectively. Here's a sample of some back-and-forth that might or might not occur as you try to ward off the claim of enabling:

"Mindful emotional eating – as I have noted previously – doesn't have to mean emotional over-eating. If you came home after a long day and are stressed out of your mind, all you want to do is to kick back, have a cup of tea and a cookie, and chill, why shouldn't you be able to do exactly that? You might say: I should be able to cope without eating. Ok. When you are able to cope without eating, then do cope without eating. But what about now? What about this moment when you feel totally fried? What are you going to do for self-care now with the resources at hand? Once again, you might say: I should hit the gym, work the stress off. You might say: I should meditate. Great. If the gym is still open, go. But if it's still open but you just can't force yourself to do one more thing after a long, tiring day, what will you do? Force yourself to meditate? Meditation doesn't work that way, you know. How are going to take care of yourself then?

Once again, you might say: "Well, I should just tough it out, white-knuckle my way through it." Nonsense. Why should you white-knuckle your way through it? White-knuckling your way through life is how you get exhausted in the first place. Why shouldn't you take this simple step of controlled self- indulgence? Why is it that you can't allow yourself this simple coping short-cut? You might say: "Because I don't trust myself to stop; I know that if I start, I won't be able to stop." Exactly. That's exactly what I am trying to help you learn to do. That is exactly the ability that I am trying to en-able with mindful emotional eating. And how will you cultivate this ability to stop and not overeat and not overdo if you don't practice? You can't just develop this ability in some parallel world. You have to field-test it here, in this life, in the life in which you do your best even if your best isn't to your liking, until your best begins to approximate the kind of best that you have in mind. I'd like for you to learn to take an occasional coping short-cut without getting totally lost in some "I blew it/I might as well go all the way" emotional eating binge. If you don't allow yourself to now and then experiment with mindful, responsible, middle-way, self-accepting, moderation-style emotional eating, then how will you ever develop this ability? I know it's a bit scary. I know you struggle to trust yourself with food. Yes, it's scary. And I'd like to enable you to stop fearing food and to use it as an occasional tool – as one of many in your coping repertoire – with moderation."

Previewing the Future: Prerequisite Skills and Attitudes

So, here's what your client needs to fine-tune his or her emotional eating to make it more mindful and, therefore, more effective:

- existential courage, open mind, and self-acceptance
- effective relaxation, increased baseline of choice awareness, and craving control skills
- a mindful emotional eating partnership

This would be a good place to include a comment I stumbled upon on the internet. A blogger named Melissa (Too Much on Her Plate http:// toomuchonherplate.com/mindful-emotional-eating-food-for-thought/) posted a complimentary comment about my approach to emotional eating with a link to my article on this humanistic harm reduction approach to emotional eating. And she invited her readers to read and comment. One of her readers, a P.W. replied with the following:

> *"Regarding the emotional eating – I don't think I need to read his book to understand emotional eating. This is only my opinion of course, but if you are not hungry and you are eating – then you are trying to fill a need with food. I have been overcoming emotional eating for years – I keep an emotional eating journal and whenever I eat other than mealtime I log in my food journal. I am not hungry [so then] why do I want to eat? Anyone who has lost weight or is in the process of losing weight has to overcome this battle with the mind and food. If we were in control of our choice to eat then we would not be overweight."*

If this comment sounds like it's coming from a closed mind, it is not. P.W.'s mind is not closed, it's afraid. That's why I put existential courage ahead of the open mind. There is no open mind when you are afraid. P.W. is afraid – we can tell that she is from key words: she's been "battling" to "overcome" emotional eating "for years." This comment is a classic sample of what you, as a clinician, will have to work with (with, not against). Your job is to help this kind of mind feel safe. How? By validating, de-pathologizing and normalizing emotional eating. And only then will this mind open up to the possibility that emotional eating doesn't have to be fought like a battle or overcome like a curse. Only then will the ice of abstinence be broken – and not over years but over months and maybe even just weeks. It's the white-knuckling that takes years to firm up into a frozen, rigid, psychologically arthritic fist of abstinence. Skillpower, harm reduction and moderation are more fluid and take less time. Which is why, in previewing the experiential part of MEE, it is essential that you make sure that your client understands that you have some very specific skills and techniques to share.

What about existential courage, open mind and self-acceptance? At this point, you will assume the existential courage, and you will work hard in Step 1 to leverage some openness of the mind. Your compassion and acceptance of client's past and present will serve as an implicit catalyst to self-acceptance. In Part II you will be offered some ideas on long-term work with emotional eating presentation. One of the chapters will deal directly with how to leverage self-acceptance. As for developing mindful emotional eating partnerships, this too is a long-term project that transcends the initial intervention. In Part II you will be presented with a discussion of how to methodically go about helping your client develop such partnerships. But initially, you, the clinician, are your client's mindful emotional eating partner. Worry not, as an MEE partner you don't have to share a pizza in a tree house under a starry night. We are talking about a different kind of partnership – a partnership of fellow minds. And that you are. That's built-in.

Key Points & Going Forward

What do you do next? That depends on who you are. If you are a self-help reader, keep on reading. If you are a clinician, reread this chapter with a highlighter. Make a note of various angles you'd like to include into your clinical sales pitch. And if you are a particularly eager beaver of a clinician who also likes structure, then here's a list of first session steps.

1) Once you establish that your client is interested in working on emotional eating, do a brief foray into the client's motives behind emotional eating. Ask: "Why do you think you engage in emotional eating?" While this question sounds almost rhetorical – after all, the term "emotional eating" pretty much tells the

story – it's still a useful question to pose. You get a quote of client's own words out of it, his or her own rationale of pursuing wellbeing (e.g. "to feel better, to numb out, to calm down, to quiet down my mind, to wind down").

2) Begin to validate, de-pathologize and normalize psychodydactically with a humanistic tone. Start firing off your clinical sales pitch. You might begin with: "I'd like to tell you how I see this clinically and how I approach this kind of work. I see emotional eating as coping, as a bonafide form of self-care. It is intuitive, simple. The problem is that when we do it mindlessly, we tend to overdo it. So, you might be surprised to hear that, as a clinician, I don't see emotional eating as a problem. I see emotional overeating as a problem. Put differently, I don't see emotional eating as a problem, I see mindless emotional eating as a problem. Why? Because mindless emotional eating leads to emotional overeating and that is, indeed, problematic. So, the solution as I clinically see it, is not to eliminate emotional eating altogether but to make it more mindful, more effective." Pause and see what your client thinks.

3) Tackle your client's objections (see various points that I have brought up and tackled in this chapter). Do it matter-of-factly, without defensiveness. Objections are not only normal but are very useful. Your client's objections and hesitations give you a chance to keep pitching but at a deeper level.

4) When the client seems to start edging into the so-called latitude of acceptance, shift into goal setting – state the 3-step program. Mind you, for you, the clinician this chapter is step 1 of 4. But for your client it's what follows that really represents the jumpstart. So, introduce the clinical mumbo-jumbo of "intuitive and portable relaxation training, choice awareness to leverage mindfulness and presence, and mindfulness-based relapse prevention strategy of craving control." Worry not about sounding a bit too technical here. That is expected. As a clinician you are a technician of sorts. Your client will find it reassuring that you have a method in mind and intrigued to find out all about these techniques.

5) Process client's reaction to this clinical 180. Chances are your client is pleasantly surprised, perhaps even relieved, and definitely intrigued. By asking about their reaction to this U-turn from the abstinence model, you give your client a chance to verbalize these sentiments. And that facilitates the buy-in, the internalization.

6) Homework: Explain that the approach does involve homework or, an ego-friendlier term, practice. If you have a handout that references the points you have made, share it. You can, of course, refer your clients to my writings, particularly this book or Chapter 4 of *Eating the Moment*. Or to the writings of Linda Craighead, *Appetite Awareness Workbook*. But beside that, there is really no homework at this point. I tell my clients to go home and to not fear their food or themselves, for that matter.

There's a good chance that all of this talk of mindful emotional eating and humanistic harm reduction radically contradicts just about everything you've read about emotional eating. And that's okay. In inviting you to shift this paradigm, keep in mind that none of this is really new. You are looking at time-tested ideas, ideas that are as old as the world. Remember the story of historical Buddha: He went from a life of princely indulgence to a life of an anorexic-ascetic to a final realization of the importance of Middle Way and staying away from extremes and living a life of moderation.

Never eating to cope – as I see it – is an unrealistic extreme. It's too ascetic. Too grotesque. Too self-denying. In contrast, eating to cope mindfully is Middle Way. If Buddha doesn't have the credentials of a sage to impress you, then maybe Aristotle would. He too talked about harm reduction. He called it "golden mean" and the importance of balance and non-excess. Self-restriction of eating, in general, or of eating to cope, in particular, is a set up for overeating and emotional overeating, respectively. The question is: Will we, clinicians and our clients, be a part of this new mindful-and-effective emotional eating paradigm or will we keep beating ourselves up for trying to take care of ourselves?

—❧

Chapter 2 | Emptying the Mind
(Relaxation)

Breath is our primary food.
Lorin Roche, *Breath Taking*

The breathing in and the breathing out are rice and barley
Atharvaveda (Zaehner, 1966)

Your heart speeds up a little when you inhale
(SNS activation) and slows down when you exhale (PNS arousal).
Rick Hanson & Richard Mendius, *Buddha's Brain*

Empty your mind before you fill your body.
Pavel Somov, *Reinventing the Meal*

• • • • • • •

We have a misconception about mindfulness. It's partly rooted in the semantics of the word: Mindfulness is not a fullness of the mind; it's an emptiness of the mind. A full mind can't attend to anything – it's already full (like that proverbial full cup that can take no more tea no matter how much you pour into it). A mindful mind is a mind that is empty enough to be filled with the here-and-now experience. So, if your client is to make a shift from mindless emotional eating to mindful emotional eating, they have to learn to empty their mind. Relaxation is one way to do it and that's what this chapter is about. Relaxation is the first course of the mindful emotional meal (MEM). Relaxation is also connecting to one's body. Mind empties itself by noticing the body around it. Read on to see exactly what I mean by all of this.

Popping the Hood

Chapter 2 is about your first experiential jumpstart step. It's akin to popping the hood. You and your client are rolling up the sleeves and getting to the business of skill training. But, first, let's recap. MEE starts off with a radical rethinking of emotional eating. Emotional eating is first de-pathologized and then re-instated as a legitimate and intuitive form of self-care, and as a potentially effective platform of coping and emotional self-regulation. And, following this humanistic reframing of the emotional eating, client is offered a clear clinical objective: "Our goal is not to eliminate emotional eating but to make it more mindful, more effective." So, that's the first order of business in this program of mindful emotional eating retraining. The second order of clinical business is relaxation training. Which is what this chapter is about.

Keep in mind, however, that while this chapter is about relaxation training only, relaxation training is not the only item on the agenda of the second session. To clarify, MEE is 4 sessions. The first session is psycho-educational. The second session is about relaxation training and training in choice-awareness and pattern interruption (see Chapter 3). So, before you proceed with relaxation training, at the outset of the second session, let your client know that you will spend the first half of the session on relaxation training and that you will be talking about choice awareness and pattern interruption in the latter part of the second session.

Oronasal Relaxation Platform

Each clinical population seems to benefit from a slightly different relaxation approach. While the basics are fundamentally the same, the specific behavioral packaging of how you get to a place of peace varies. In working with emotional eating clients, I favor the following types of relaxation techniques:

- Humming
- Mmm-ing
- Toning
- Sighing
- Pursed lips breathing
- Smelling
- Water drinking
- Touching lips
- Chewing gum
- Tongue locking/Jihva Bandha
- Pure Breath Focus/Anapanasati

This relaxation package for emotional eating utilizes the oronasal hardware of eating – that of the mouth and the nose, whereas the relaxation package for anger management, in contrast, works with the anatomical hardware of fighting (with the help of the "open your hand to open your mind" relaxation technique).

Relaxation Habit

But customization of relaxation doesn't stop there. Additionally, this particular relaxation package, as you will see in a moment, underscores the importance of tuning in to the sensations that accompany eating. In selecting these particular relaxation techniques, I was guided by the following criteria:

- Simplicity
- Multi-utility
- Packability
- Portability

These four elements assure the development of a relaxation habit.

Simplicity

Simplicity, in the case of relaxation training, has to do with bottom-up rather than the top-down route of emotional self-regulation. Guided imagery or de-catastrophizing would be examples of a "top-down" route to self-regulation. Having your clients think about relaxing in order to relax – that would be top-down and top-down takes time. To relax through, say, guided imagery takes time and it places a certain amount of cognitive load on an otherwise resource-depleted mind. What we need is an intuitive relaxation shortcut that requires little or no analysis. What we need is a "bottom-up" relaxation shortcut. "Bottom-up" here means non-conceptual, non-central, and non-cognitive. In other words, "bottom-up" means peripheral: Changing the state of the body to change the state of the mind rather than working this connection in reverse.

Multi-utility

Furthermore, we want to make maximum use – double use, if not triple use – out of any given relaxation pathway. For example, a mere act of drinking water 1) works to relax, 2) works to preload (for an earlier onset of fullness), 3) works as a convenient way to prime for the sensations of fullness (to promote awareness of satiety). That's three utilities out of one method. Similarly, an act of conscious smelling 1) works to slow you down (which takes you off the mindless eating autopilot), 2) acts to relax you (since smelling is a form of conscious breathing), 3) serves as an essential aspect of savoring (which leverages the mindfulness process), 4) and allows you to preload as well (by creating a sense of fullness). That's four utilities out of one relaxation activity. That's some impressive multi-utility for you.

Packability

You know how when you pack for a trip you might stuff a pair of fresh socks into each one of your shoes. You do so to maximize space. Why not use the same kind of packing mentality when you go on a relaxation journey? So, by packability I mean the ability of one relaxation path to "fold into" another relaxation path so as to create a relaxation combo. Being able to do so is a kind of clinical origami, an art of folding multiple behaviors into one. For example, one of my relaxation combos involves a "noseful" of conscious smelling on the way in (as you inhale) and a foodgasmic "mmm-ful" of savoring on the way out (as you exhale). The details are to follow but at this point I only mean to illustrate that it pays to pack together (combine) various multi-utility relaxation paths into a kind of relaxation power-punch.

Portability

The marriage of multi-utility and packability results in portability. The end goal of relaxation training is to help your client develop a relaxation habit. Therefore, the relaxation technique needs to be portable, easy to use in public, and, preferably, as inconspicuous as possible. We don't just stress-eat at home: There is a lot of emotional eating that happens in the work place. Thus, portability is essential. An intuitively simple, conceptually face valid, well-packaged, multi-use, portable relaxation combo is well positioned for conditioning and habit formation.

Semantic Cue-Conditioning

Effective habit-formation thrives on cues. The relaxation meme here is "Relaxation is the first course (of mindful emotional eating)." And "Empty your mind before you fill up your belly." As you present all of the different relaxation shortcuts, keep reiterating this relaxation narrative that has been customized to the challenge of emotional eating. Merely saying "Relax." isn't enough. What we want to do, as clinicians, is to help our clients embrace a more integrated view of mindful emotional eating. By framing *relaxation as the first course of the mindful emotional meal* and by inviting your client to *empty their mind with relaxation before they fill up their belly* we help our clients develop a more methodical view of mindful emotional eating.

No Self-Tricking

Before you present your client with this oronasal relaxation package it is important to clarify that we are not trying to trick ourselves out of emotional eating. We are not playing a game of postponement. Relaxation is to be viewed as a bonafide first course of the mindful emotional eating meal, not a substitute for it. Naturally, if your client feels after the first course of relaxation that they don't need to eat to cope anymore, they don't have to proceed. If they feel that they are experientially full, that they have lost their appetite for emotional eating, that they are good to go now, then so be it. But this should not in any way be a goal. And this is essential to reiterate. Relaxation-as-the-first-course should not be misused as relaxation-as-the-only-course.

Now let's take a closer look at the different oronasal relaxation paths available to us. And then we'll talk about how to combine these stand-alone relaxation shortcuts into simple, portable relaxation power-punches.

Prolonged Exhalation

Taking a deep breath when stressed seems like age-old advice. But it's frequently misapplied. Typically, when we, as clinicians, offer deep breathing as a relaxation technique, we place the emphasis on the in breath, on the inhalation phase of the breath cycle, on taking a deep breath. But that's not really where the relaxation and stress-diffusing effect lies. The relaxing part of conscious breathing is on the back end of the breath cycle, in the prolongation of the out breath. How do you prolong the exhalation phase of the breath cycle? By taking a longer time to exhale (e.g. with the help of counting) or by narrowing the oronasal aperture through which you exhale (e.g. exhaling through your nose or pursed lips).

Nasal Breathing and Nitric Oxide

Did you know that humming and chanting doesn't just feel good but actually does good? I wrote about this *best-kept secret of relaxation training* in my 2012 book, *Reinventing the Meal*:

Nasal humming (and chanting, for that matter) triggers the release of a substantial amount of nitric oxide (NO). What's the significance of this? Louis Ignarro, distinguished professor of pharmacology at the UCLA School of Medicine and a 1998 Nobel Prize laureate for his discovery of the importance of nitric oxide, describes NO as "the body's natural cardiovascular wonder drug" (2005, xiii). According to a report in the *American Journal of Respiratory and Critical Care Medicine*, "The paranasal sinuses are major producers of nitric oxide (NO)." The researchers hypothesized that "oscillating airflow produced by humming would enhance sinus ventilation and thereby increase nasal NO levels" (Weitzberg & Lundberg, 2002, 144). Indeed, their study found that humming increased nasal NO by a factor of fifteen when compared to quiet exhalation. Why is this of any relevance? Because nitric oxide release happens to both accompany and power up the relaxation effect. Here's what the godfather of Western relaxation research, Herbert Benson, MD, had to say about nitric oxide in his book *Relaxation Revolution*: "Those practicing mind-body techniques [tend] to experience lower blood pressure, calmer brain activity, healthful emissions of nitric oxide in the body's cells and other physical and emotional benefits" (Benson & Proctor, 2010, 22). Benson explains that "release of nitric oxide in the body's cells ... serves as a vasodilator, an agent that expands blood vessels. This dilation process can be highly effective in reducing blood pressure" (129). He also explains that nitric oxide is "associated with good health, including antibacterial and antiviral responses and also beneficial changes in the cardiovascular system" (77).

Prolonged Exhalation of the Nasal Type

I distinguish three types of nasal prolonged exhalation breathing: humming, mmm-ing, and moaning. I don't recommend moaning but it serves as a good way to introduce mmm-ing.

Humming

You don't have to use mental count to prolong exhalation. Frankly, the business of mental counting feels like a hassle. A simpler, more enjoyable, and more bottom-up (non-cognitive) way to prolong the out-breath is to *hum* it out. Invite your client to try to exhale several breaths through the nose while humming. Model it in session as part of relaxation training. Have a few "humfuls" to appreciate the subtle soothing vibration of humming. And invite your client to have a few humfuls before they have a few mouthfuls. Say:

> *"Next time you feel like you want to eat to cope, have a few humful breaths first. Fill up on relaxation. Humfuls first, mouthfuls second. Empty your mind with a few humfuls before you fill up your belly."*

Moaning & Mmm-ing

Moaning needs no introduction. We moan in pain. We moan as we struggle and endure. Therefore, moaning has an affectively negative valence. And I do not recommend it as a relaxation path in the context of mindful emotional eating. Moaning is however very similar to mmm-ing in terms of its vocal execution so take a moment to moan for a moment or two, just as a warm-up for mmm-ing.

Mmm-ing as a mantra of gustatory enjoyment – a kind of "om" of mindful eating. Indeed, the sound "mmm" is the music of savoring, the sound of eating satisfaction associated with the so-called foodgasms, a celebration of gustatory pleasure (Somov, 2008). So, introduce this curious oronasal relaxation strategy to your emotional eating client and explain:

> *"You don't have to wait until you have something in your mouth to "mmm" about. You can also amplify the pleasure of anticipation. And that's where mmm-ing comes in as a double-use relaxation short-cut. Mmm-ing is a form of nasal prolongation of exhalation and a subjective amplification of eating satisfaction. Try mmm-ing now to see what I mean about the extended out-breath."*

Clinician, there is a good chance that your client might feel a bit self-conscious about making this arguably emotionally intimate sound in session. So, it's best if you model some mmm-ing to demo the prolonged exhalation aspect of it. And then cap off the moment with the following recommendation:

> *"Before you eat to cope, mmm a little. Empty your mind with a bit of mmm-ing before you fill up your belly. Have a few mmm-fuls for your first course of relaxation. Prime yourself for eating pleasure to leverage more coping per calorie."*

Prolonged Exhalation Breathing of Oral Type

Just like you can extend the exhalation phase of your breath cycle through nasal breathing, you can also prolong your breath by breathing out through your mouth. I distinguish three types of extending your out-breath orally – toning, sighing, and exhaling through pursed lips.

Toning

Don Campbell, the founder of the Institute of Music, Health and Education, says this about toning: "Toning balances brain waves, deepens the breath, reduces the heart rate and imparts a general sense of well-being" (2001, p. 93). Toning is elongation of vowels and thus, fundamentally, a form of prolonged exhalation. According to Campbell, toning ahhh evokes an immediate relaxation response, and toning om – the richest tonal phoneme – can even warm skin temperature (Amen, 1998). Daniel Amen, in his book Change Your Brain, Change Your Life, recommends toning for five minutes a day as a stress management tool. And I, in turn, recommend toning as yet another relaxation shortcut as part of the first course of mindful emotional eating. Invite your client to tone a few ahhhs or a few oms to fill up on relaxation before filling up on food.

Sighing

Another oral way to extend the exhalation phase is sighing. Sighing is intuitive for the body. We sigh at a moment of emotional relief. But we don't have to wait till some crisis or stressor is over in order for us to sigh in relief. You can sigh on demand. Invite your client to sigh a few times to see how it works. There is a kind of energetic but brief uptake of air and a prolonged exhalation through a loosely protruding mouth. There is a characteristic "wooh" sound to it. Or a more open "ahh" sound to it. The "wooh" takes longer than "ahh." So, I recommend the "wooh" since it prolongs the out-breath better than "ahh." Encourage your clients to experiment with issuing some preventive sighs of release as an intuitive relaxation shortcut. Say:

> "Empty your mind with a few sighs of relief before you sit down to eat to cope. The more stress you relieve with sighing the less stress there is to cope with by eating."

Pursed Lips Exhalation

Breathing out through pursed lips is similar to sighing. The difference is that the oral aperture is more tightly controlled. When you sigh your lips are slack. When you breath out through pursed lips, lips are held more tightly, the opening of the mouth is narrower, and as a result the out-breath is even longer. Try to breathe out through pursed lips. Invite your client to empty his or her mind before eating with a few such breaths.

Smelling

Smelling is the opposite of prolonged exhalation. Smelling is a long inhalation. When you take a purposeful whiff, you take a long draw of air. If we go with the theory about prolonged exhalation, then smelling in and of itself would seem counterproductive. A longer inhalation is arousing rather than calming. But there is a way for your client to use smelling as a way to relax before eating. And we have a good reason to try to take advantage of smelling: Much of the sensation of taste is powered by the nose rather than the tongue. And we are definitely interested in making an emotional eating episode richer in taste so as to hopefully keep it from being larger in calories. Furthermore, smelling has been indicated as a way to preload on fullness. Taking conscious *nosefuls* of the food's aroma allows you to experience a sooner onset of fullness and, therefore, not overeat. So, we have many good reasons to incorporate smelling into the first course of relaxation. Encourage your client to combine *nosefuls* with *mmm-fuls* or with *hum-fuls*. The idea here is to take a long conscious noseful of food smells on the in-breath and mmm on the out-breath. That's it. Try it to see what I mean. Tell your client:

> *"How about you practice this next time you sit down to eat to cope.*
> *Set out some food in front of you but before you eat, have a first course*
> *of relaxation by inhaling the smell and mmm-ing it out in satisfaction.*
> *In – the smell, out – the sound of fulfilling satisfaction."*

Water Drinking

Your lungs and your stomach share the same portal. But your body is smart; it knows how to handle these two very different kinds of traffic – water and air. So, when you take a sip of any liquid your body pauses your breath to make sure that the liquid doesn't do down the wrong pipe. Encourage your client to experiment with this. Tell them to drink a glass of water before they eat to cope and to notice how the body slows itself down by pausing the breath to accommodate a sip. Another rationale for drinking water as the first course of relaxation has to do with the fact that preloading on water facilitates a sooner onset of fullness. Additionally, research suggests that preloading by drinking just two eight-ounce glasses of water before a meal may help with weight-loss success (Davy et al., 2008). Another reason for drinking water to relax is that dehydration reduces the activity of nitric oxide synthase, an enzyme that converts the amino acid L-arginine into nitric oxide, that miracle molecule of relaxation; and hydration reverses this process (Bryan and Zand, 2010). Finally, mindfully drinking a glass of water allows you to experience the sensation of abdominal distention, i.e. the physiological signature of fullness. Therefore, drinking water not only relaxes and facilitates the onset of fullness through preloading, but it also primes your client's mind for paying attention to the sensations of fullness.

So, what we have here is a bottom-up, NO-enhancing, filling, awareness-building, portable relaxation shortcut. After you present the rationale behind this relaxation shortcut, simply say:

> *"Next time you sit down to eat to cope, have a glass of water, take*
> *your time with it. Empty a glass of water to empty your mind."*

Also encourage your client to experiment with drinking *warm* water, drinking a warm glass of milk, or drinking a cup of something non-caffeinated. I would particularly like to highlight chamomile tea as a simple oronasal relaxation shortcut. I playfully call chamomile "calm-omile" because of its calming effects. So, bottoms up.

Touching Lips

Rick Hanson and Richard Mendius, in their 2009 book, *Buddha's Brain*, write: "Parasympathetic fibers are spread throughout your lips; thus, touching your lips stimulates the PNS. Touching your lips can also bring up soothing associations of eating or even of breastfeeding when you were a baby" (p. 82). Could this be the secret behind the good romantic kiss? Maybe. Definitely something to think about, right? But for our purposes, touching the lips seems like a perfect oronasal relaxation shortcut before eating. Encourage your client to try running his or her index finger along the track of their lips a few relaxing and self-soothing laps. Alternatively, you could have your client apply a few massaging rounds of flavored lip balm and sit for a few minutes in breath focus. And finally, a simple act of moistening the lips with the tongue can too serve as a way to stimulate the relaxing effect of the PNS.

Chewing Gum

Emotional eating is a form of self-pacification. And you can think of chewing gum as an adult pacifier. Chewing gum, particularly flavored gum, engages your oronasal apparatus, thus engaging the parasympathetic nervous system (PNS) and positioning you for relaxation. With this in mind, encourage your client to stock up on some of the modern-day intriguing chewing gum options. Invite them to relax with a few minutes of chewing gum before they eat to cope. As you know gum loses flavor relatively fast. After a couple of minutes the flavor is more or less gone and we feel kind of bummed out, but here it's actually good news: The loss of gum's flavor is a natural way to time the duration of relaxation.

Tongue Lock/Jihva Bandha

Tongue lock is when you curl up the tip of your tongue to touch your palate and you keep it that way for a while. This kind of tongue lock is a part of yoga breath practices and is called *jihva bandha*. When used as part of a breathing meditation, jihva bandha can also involve a slight stretching of frenulum (which is the bridle that connects your tongue to the floor of your mouth). Try to curl up your tongue right now so that it not only touches the palate but curves back. Strain yourself a bit. The stretch you feel is your frenulum. Combine this tongue-lock with a noseful of smell as you inhale and with an mmm-ful out-breath as you exhale. Packing so much into a single breath cycle – a noseful, a tongue lock, and an mmm-ful is a sensation-rich experience. Tongue-lock is a potent concentration practice; it preoccupies the mind in doing so empties the mind of stress. If you do this for a minute or so, you will soon notice that there is some accumulation of saliva. Swallow it and re-lock yourself into this oronasal concentration combo for another moment or two.

Breath Focus/Anapanasati

Anapanasati is pure breath focus, mere awareness of breathing as it is. This has always made sense to me: The body knows how to breathe and it really needs no direction from you. The *pranayama* approach to breathing is about modifying, shaping, and changing your breathing rate. Anapanasati is simpler and harder than pranayama. Anapanasati is simple because there is nothing to do and it is hard because there is nothing to do. And we are not very good at doing nothing. But if your client can allow himself or herself to do nothing, they will likely find it rather liberating. So, simply instruct:

> *"When you sit down to eat to cope, take a couple of moments to simply notice your breath exactly as it is. There is nothing else required of you in this moment. Notice your breath to empty your mind before you proceed to fill up your belly."*

10 Relaxation Combos

There are many different ways to combine these relaxation shortcuts. Here are a few that I like (in no particular order):

- a noseful (of smell) on the in-breath + a hum-ful (of self-soothing) on the out-breath
- a noseful (of smell) on the in-breath + an mmm-ful (of satisfaction) on the out-breath
- either of the above with a tongue lock
- a sip (of water) + a hum-ful (of self-soothing) on the out-breath (do this through a full glass of water)
- a sip (of water) + a wooh-like sigh (of relief) on the out-breath (do this through a full glass of water)
- a noseful (of smell) on the in-breath + toning -ee or -aa on the out-breath
- humming with a tongue lock
- mmm-ing with a tongue lock
- anapanasati/breath focus + jihva bandha/tongue lock
- drinking a glass of water punctuated with anapanasati/breath focus in between sips

Try all of these combos yourself before you offer them to your clients. Learn the lingo and the mechanics so that you can explain these novel oronasal maneuvers. If you don't have much time, just go with the basics – some plain breath focus, maybe a humful or two, maybe a glass of water. Help your client play around with these ideas to develop a relaxation ritual of their own. And, of course, if you as a clinician have your own field-tested way of relaxation training, use it. The core idea here is not the "how" of relaxation but the mere fact of it as the first course of a mindful emotional eating meal.

A Power-Combo: Air + Water = First MEE Course

Encourage your client to have some air and to have some water. It doesn't have to be either/or. Why air first and water second? We are just following the survival priorities, that's all. An intuitive sequence. But of course, if you are using a combo (of sipping through a glass of water with humming or sighing or toning or mmm-ing in between) then the two become one. Insisting on both tactics (of breathing and drinking water) buys your client more time to wind down, allows them to preload (through smelling and with liquids), and helps them tune in to the eating apparatus.

Process Focus Sensitization

Oronasal relaxation shortcuts prime the client's mind to tune in to the olfactory and gustatory stimuli associated with eating and that is value-added. Relaxing in this oronasal manner (as opposed to, say, sitting in a massage chair or taking a shower or using some musculoskeletal relaxation sequence or some imagery) is meant to drive the client's mind towards the process of mindful eating. These relaxation techniques recalibrate your client's attention away from cognition back to sensation. Your client doesn't want to think anymore. He or she is fried, beat, stressed. They are looking for a way to connect with their body and to find solace in the unambiguous richness of sensation. And that's where the proposed relaxation package comes in – this particular kind of relaxation platform not only relaxes but also primes the mind for mindful eating. The idea here is not only to empty the mind of stress but to also awaken the mind to the oronasal landscape of eating sensations.

Time Management
(on Both Sides of the Clinical Dynamic)

There are three issues here: one from clinician and two from clients. Since this book is primarily for clinicians, let's tackle the clinical objection of time management first. A clinician might object: "Pavel, this is too much – too many relaxation skills to teach to the client." Agreed, this is a big chapter, but it's not that big of a job. 15 to 30 minutes max when you know what you are doing. You don't have to present your client with all of these relaxation shortcuts. Just present a few, roll them into a relaxation power-punch and you are done. Maybe give your client a handout and homework to experiment with whatever strikes their fancy. That's about it.

Now, the client on the other hand might challenge you with an oldie-but-goodie: "I don't have time." If so, simply counter this objection with: "Yes, you do: if you have time to cope by eating, you have time to relax. Take your time to relax before you eat to cope so as to not waste more time on mindless overeating."

The client might also ask you to be more specific about how much time to spend on relaxation. What I usually say is: "The more time you take to relax, the less stress you have to cope with by eating." But after explaining this inverted correlation, I paradoxically rush to add:

> *"But don't spend too much time in relaxation, maybe 5 minutes tops – I don't want for you to start feeling like you are trying to trick yourself out of emotional eating. Sure, if after a few minutes of relaxation you conclude that you no longer feel like eating to cope, then, naturally, you don't have to. But if, after a few minutes of relaxation, you feel better but you still want to do some emotional eating, then there is no point in continuing to relax in the hope that you can dodge emotional eating altogether."*

Key Points & Going Forward

There are many different ways of presenting this first experiential training step. Here are some general ways for framing this first behavioral step:

- Relaxation is the first course of the mindful emotional eating meal.

- First course of mindful emotional eating is to connect to your body with relaxation.

- Empty your mind with relaxation before you fill up your belly.

- First, empty your mind by connecting to your body. And then you can eat.

- Practice relaxation-as-the-first-course not only when you decided to eat to cope but any time you eat.

Use these ideas as clinical refrains as you introduce your client to the relaxation training. But also feel free to develop your own way of pitching relaxation to your emotional eating client. And make sure that your client gets the core rationale for why a mindful emotional eating episode should begin with relaxation. Keep reiterating that by reducing the amount of stress on the front end, before eating, your client will have less stress to cope with by eating. Relaxation-as-the-first-course positions your client to have a successful emotional eating experience. Relaxation-as-the first-course enables emotional eating in moderation.

Chapter 3 | Waking Up the Mind & Keeping It Awake
(Choice Awareness Training & Pattern Interruption)

A mindful emotional eating episode begins with connecting to your body (through relaxation) and proceeds with connecting to your mind (through choice awareness and pattern interruption). Choice Awareness Training (CAT) is used to both awaken the mind before you eat to cope and to keep it awake while you eat to cope. The initial awakening of the mind is accomplished through a choice awareness ritual and the subsequent keeping the mind awake is accomplished with the help of pattern interruption. You use a choice awareness ritual to kick the closed door of the mind wide open and then you use pattern interruption to keep it ajar. This chapter will introduce you to the clinical rationale behind choice awareness training and to the experiential nuts and bolts of sharing this mindfulness know-how with your client.

A Note to Clinician:
We Are Still in Session 2

Before we continue, let us reorient ourselves to where we are in this clinical curriculum for mindful emotional eating. In Session 1 of MEE you reframe the problem to reframe the solution – in other words, you introduce the humanistic harm reduction approach to dealing with the issue of emotional eating. Then comes Session 2. Session 2 shifts the client into a skill-building stance. There are two main items on the agenda for Session 2: Relaxation Training and Choice Awareness Training. We talked about Relaxation Training in Chapter 2 and now we will discuss Choice Awareness Training. Worry not, once you figure out the nuts and bolts of this protocol, you'll have plenty of time to squeeze both into one clinical hour (if you have to). Without any further programmatic ado, now let us focus on Choice Awareness Training. Some of what follows is clinically expositional, just for you, clinician. The rest is for your clients' ears.

One more preview point to help you stay oriented: Whereas relaxation is the first course of mindful emotional eating, choice awareness is the second course of a mindful emotional eating meal. First, your client connects to his or her body with relaxation, and then he or she connects to his or her mind. Put differently, first the client empties one's mind of stress by connecting to one's body, and then he or she awakens his or her mind and keeps it awake with choice awareness and pattern interruption. And now we are ready to proceed.

Mindfulness Is Choice Awareness,
Choice Awareness is Mindfulness

In the context of eating, we are used to talking about mindfulness of taste, i.e. savoring. The mindfulness we are talking about here is different – it's the mindfulness of the process of eating. But what is a process? A process of any kind is a series of real-time decisions, a dynamic encounter of reality in which you actively navigate various subtle decisional crossroads. This is hard when you are awake. And it's pretty much impossible when you are asleep, i.e. mindless. When you are mindless, you make no choices, you are just flying on autopilot. You default to your habits. Your habits preempt choices. Your habits spare you the hard work of making choices. And making choices is work. So, in this context, we will define mindfulness as choice awareness, as decisional awareness, as conscious, mindful acting rather than unconscious, mindless reacting.

We could say that the mind is lazy. But it really isn't. Mind is economical. Mind is conservative: It conserves energy and effort wherever it can. Mind doesn't like the hassle of making choices, so it decides how to proceed once and puts this self-programmed algorithm of action on autopilot, leaving the dirty work of executing a series of trivial mini-choices to the memory of the body. Let me clarify: The body makes no choices, the body simply obeys the past directives, running on feedback loops.

Thus, mindlessness is re-activity, not conscious activity but re-activity, a re-enactment of what was once decided and put on autopilot. All this is adaptive, of course. And we pay for this adaptation with mindlessness. And sometimes we end up overpaying. Once a behavior goes on autopilot it tends to stay there. Going off the autopilot is a mini-shock of sorts, a pattern break, and, as such, a mini-awakening of sorts. The cost of going off the autopilot is a bit of confusion and some behavioral awkwardness. And that is exactly what we are after because it is exactly in this confusion and awkwardness that mindfulness is forged.

Eating is arguably the most overlearned voluntary behavior in the human repertoire of skills. As I've watched my toddler eat over the past two years, I see the creative, conscious, mindful trial and error, gradually giving way to the emerging learning curve. My daughter's eating has been so far all hers: She drinks by dipping her fingers into water and licks them off. She sees fries as delivery vehicles for ketchup. She follows no rules yet. She is inventing eating on her own. But invariably all of these creative experiments will eventually give way to cultural programming. Even if we don't tell her how to eat, she'll pick it up through observation. Monkey see, monkey do, you know. Her inherently mindful eating will eventually go on autopilot and she will stop making choices. Until, of course, one day she makes a choice to wake up and to start making choices.

If mindfulness is choice awareness or choice-ful-ness, then mindlessness is un-awareness of choice or choice-less-ness. And choice-less-ness, as the term implies, is a loss of freedom. Your job, as an MEE clinician, is to help your client regain this freedom of choice, to help your client infuse some choice-ful-ness into his or her mindless eating.

The Choice Circle

Let's talk specifics now (and we'll take a closer look at the clinical rationale behind choice awareness training [CAT] later). Here's the core experience that I always use to demonstrate CAT. For this to work, for you to quickly see what I am talking about, you need to work through this little exercise, just as it's presented next. If you don't try it but just read through it, you'll most likely be wasting your time. Trust me. (The way I present it here to you is how you would present it to your client.)

You'll need three sheets of paper and a pen. Sticky notes work best for this exercise. If you are reading this book in print, I have left several blank spaces below specifically for this exercise.

Instructions:

- Draw a circle on the first paper (or in the first blank space below).
- Draw another circle on the second piece of paper (or in the second blank space below).
- Draw one more circle on the third (last) piece of paper (or in the last space below).

Draw a circle:

Draw a circle:

Draw a circle:

Look at these circles. What stands out? Chances are, the circles are pretty similar to each other in terms of placement on the page, diameter, starting point, and direction (clockwise or counterclockwise) of the drawing. Right? If so, what do you make of all this similarity? Did you *consciously* intend for these circles to be similar? Probably not. The circles have been drawn too mindlessly, too reflexively, too reactively, too mechanically, too compulsively, too robotically, too reactively (i.e., too unconsciously) for you to take the credit for this action. They just sort of "happened," like the things we say or do in our relationships – on autopilot. To clarify, the decision to comply with this exercise was, of course, yours. Yes, you did decide to go ahead and try this out. But the actual shape, the configuration of the circles, the way they were drawn – that just sort of happened as a kind of circle-drawing reaction, as a reenactment of some circle- drawing habit from the past, without a conscious or mindful deliberation. This exercise gives you a sense of what life on autopilot is like.

Now, let's toss a monkey wrench into this mindlessness. Let's break a pattern. Let's wake you up from your circle-drawing autopilot: Draw another circle, but mindfully, consciously, with awareness (on a blank piece of paper or in the space that follows). *Choose* where to place the circle on the page. *Choose* where you want to start the circle. *Choose* in which direction you will draw the circle. *Choose* how big or small you want to make it.

Draw a circle now:

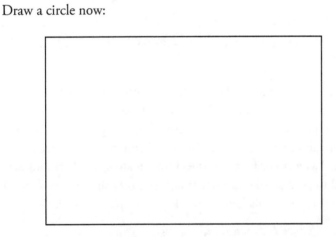

How was this task? How did the experience of drawing the last circle compare with the experience of drawing the first three circles? Did you like feeling conscious, being mindful, being in control, feeling present? How do you think this feeling might be useful to you and your client in life in general and, more specifically, in managing anger?

Now, take a moment to imagine walking a client through this exercise the second time you see him or her. Imagine the pleasant surprise on clients' faces when the proverbial light bulb goes off in their heads: The experience of presence, of being fully in the moment, of consciously owning one's here- and- now behavior is a powerful existential highlight. Many of my clients would use such loaded words as "feeling enlightened" or "having an epiphany." So, take another moment to imagine the potential impact of giving your client this kind of experience of awakening. Anger management will never be the same after that. Choice awareness, in my experience, is a lubricant of clinical progress (more about this follows).

Clinical Rationale:
Change Equation and Operational Freedom

This part is for you, the clinician. It's a bit heavy on theory; the idea is not to overwhelm you but to give you a panoramic overview of all that's happening as part of CAT. This was developed in 2000 as part of an overall change model called Change Equation (Somov & Somova, 2003). Over the years, I have used this method extensively with substance use problems, perfectionism, overeating, smoking cessation, and, of course, anger. CAT is one of the three variables of the process of change that can be summarized as the following equation:

> Change = Reason to Change + Freedom to Change + Method to Change

Reason to change is the "why," the motivation behind the change process. Method to change is the "how," the skillpower necessary to carry out the change process (impulse control, for example). Freedom to change is the minimal baseline of mindfulness and conscious presence necessary to activate the "why" in order to do the "how" in any given here and now. CAT is designed to awaken the zombie, to take you off mindless autopilot, to help your mind shrug off maladaptive, outdated autopilot modes.

Freedom to Choose Is Freedom to Change

When we talk about choices, we talk about freedom. There is no freedom to change without making conscious choices. To reprogram, you have to be free. If you are an anger zombie, on an autopilot of trigger-happy overreaction, you will not experience change or reprogramming. You are asleep at the wheel, stuck in a vicious interpersonal loop. You have to first wake up; you have to awaken the programmer. And then, you have to keep waking yourself up so as to develop a new baseline of presence. Realize that freedom begins with awareness, and freedom to change begins with choice awareness.

Understanding the Choice Process

Once again, freedom manifests through the awareness of a choice. But what is a choice? Choice is an awareness process. We say we "have a choice" when we are aware of options from which to select. Thus, the notion of "choice" refers to the following:

- The awareness of the options available
- The actual act of selection from one of the available options

Becoming aware of the options restores our sense of freedom, takes us off autopilot, off zombie mode, and gives us an opportunity to change our patterns, habits, rituals, and routines.

Theoretical Freedom vs. Operational Freedom

In theory, we are free. And yet, we do not feel free. We mindlessly and unconsciously repeat the same old stimulus-response patterns over and over. No wonder we feel stuck in a vicious cycle and feel powerless to change. Operational (actionable) freedom is exactly proportionate to our choice awareness, to our mindfulness of the options that we have. The more options we are aware of at any given moment, *the freer* we are. Thus, the goal of choice awareness training is to increase your client's operating freedom, his or her moment-to-moment capacity to choose how to act rather than mindlessly re-enact old coping, self-soothing defaults.

Choice Awareness as Pattern Interruption

Most of our life happens on autopilot. Autopilot is a behavioral pattern, a pattern of unconscious stimulus-response reactivity. Anger is no exception: Angry folks lash out habitually, reflexively, reactively, mindlessly, without awareness. The goal of CAT is to break these patterns, to help your clients go off the mindless emotional eating autopilot. Choice awareness would first allow your clients to become more conscious, more aware at a baseline, and then use this awareness and presence to make emotional eating more mindful.

Choice Awareness as Decisional Mindfulness

Autopilot modes spare us the effort of needing to make a choice. That's both efficient and problematic. It's efficient if the autopilot is working in our favor and problematic if it has outlived its usefulness. Change begins with a decision to change, with a choice to change. Decision is a choice. No choice means no decision. Seen as such, choice awareness is a form of decisional mindfulness.

You can say to your client:

"I am sure you've felt out of control after an episode of emotional overeating. When we operate on autopilot, when we run on reflex, we feel that life is happening to us—that we are not choosing what to do but "just doing it." Naturally, it feels like we are "out of control." We are and we aren't. We are out of control when we are mindlessly, choicelessly on autopilot (autopilot is in charge). And we aren't out of control when we get off autopilot and start consciously making real-time choices. In a sense, the goal of CAT is to reinstate ourselves as pilots, as persons in charge, as the proverbial captains of our own ships, instead of defaulting to old behavioral routines."

Choice Awareness as Deprogramming & Reprogramming

Reprogramming begins with deprogramming. Mindless emotional eating is old coping software. Mindful emotional eating is new coping software. Before we install new mindware, we have to uninstall the old mindware. Choice awareness does both: It defrags and refrags, deprograms and reprograms, uninstalls and upgrades. Choice awareness works strategically and tactically. It first awakens the programmer in you and then allows you, the programmer, to begin to rewrite your maladaptive, outdated programming. In sum, the goal of CAT is to teach your clients to deprogram the mindless eating so that they can begin to consciously reprogram themselves when they sit down to cope by eating.

Choice Awareness as Engagement with the Present

Living on autopilot is living in the past, re-living the past. CAT is designed to help you stay in the moment, to act rather than react. CAT is a commitment to the present. Help your client realize that choice awareness is a form of behavioral mindfulness, a form of process mindfulness; it's a choice to show up for the present moment, to attend to this here-and-now slice of life rather than keep burying it under piles of mindlessly consumed food.

Pattern Interruption Strategies: Keeping the Mind Awake While Eating

Help your client realize that awakening the mind is one thing and keeping the mind awake is another. Minds tend to fall asleep. While a circle-drawing exercise will come with some half-life of presence, it also helps to use what I call "pattern breaks" to keep the mind awake and on its toes. Help your client see that choice awareness training isn't just about kicking the closed door of the mind open. It's also about propping it ajar. CAT is intended as a general tonic for the mind, as a means to leveraging a greater baseline of presence while you eat to cope. Choice awareness training is pattern interruption; when you break a pattern you begin to see that you were on autopilot, that you were blind, that you didn't see what you were doing. And now you see. Thus, choice awareness training, in its pattern interruption form, restores the vision of your mind's eye. It helps you see what is. Tell your client that mindlessness is a blindness of sorts and that mindfulness is vision.

It is a good idea to customize pattern interruption techniques to fit the behavioral hardware in question. The pattern breaks that follow are designed specifically for facilitating mindful eating. Offer these pattern break exercises (meditations) to your clients as part of CAT homework.

Second Course: Connecting to Your Mind by Drawing a Circle

Invite clients to draw a mindful circle right before they start eating to cope. I call it the second course. The first course is relaxation which is a chance to connect to your body. The second course is...to take a second...to connect to your mind...by waking it up. That's all. As for technicalities, a pen and a sticky note would do. A finger on the countertop would do. A finger tracing out the edge of a plate would also do just fine. A drawing doesn't have to be a drawing.

Enso Your Way into Eating

Here's another way to draw a circle to wake yourself up before you eat. I described this first in my 2012 book, *Reinventing the Meal*. Here's how it goes:

"*Enso* is Japanese for "circle," a common subject of Zen calligraphy. An empty *enso* circle symbolizes enlightenment and the void (emptiness). Why void? Why enlightenment? An *enso* drawing, as I see it, documents the fleeting insubstantiality of the moment and the enlightened awareness of its impermanence. As such, an *enso* drawing is a pattern interrupter. It is a moment of presence, or mindfulness, and a commitment to the moment, however fleeting it might be. Most of us in the West eat off of circular plates. Next time you see the circular shape of a plate, think, "*enso*." Think, "a symbol of void and emptiness not unlike my hunger." Think, "an opportunity for awareness." Recognize the circular dish in front of you as an invaluable cue and ask yourself, "Will my next eating moment be just another mindless spin around this carousel of eating? Will it be another vicious cycle of mindless overeating? Will I spend the next ten minutes flipping through the menu circle of TV channels with untasted food in my mouth? Or will I break the pattern, select a new course, notice the moment, notice the world, touch reality, and see myself interact with it?" Before you find yourself mindlessly cleaning your plate, clean the cobwebs of routine patterns from your mind."

So, what do we have here? A kind of mnemonic devise: a plate is an enso. When you see a plate, you see an enso; when you see a plate – whether it is made of china or paper – you see an opportunity to wake up. Here's how your client can train themselves to associate an empty plate with a full mind: Suggest that they draw an enso (a circle) right on the paper plate before they place any food on it and before they start eating. A black marker on a white paper plate is a stark pattern break. As your client eats off the plate, the enso of presence will shine through with rays of enlightening awareness.

Open Your Hand to Re-Open Your Mind

Invite your client to mindfully let go of the utensils or of the foodstuff in between the bites as a way of punctuating the emotional eating with moments of choice awareness and letting go. Mindless emotional eating comes with a kind of desperate death-grip, a clinging, a grasping. Inviting your client to mindfully release this death-grip of tension is a powerful way to re-awaken yourself. This kind of physical letting go of a utensil is a great metaphor for letting go of any sense of rush to cope. Simply say:

> *"When you eat to cope next time, try to make a point to not just put the utensils down in between bites, but to also release any sense of rush and clinging to this moment. Take your time to cope. There is no rush. Open your hand to re-open, to re-awaken your mind."*

Eat with Your Non-dominant Hand

This is my favorite awareness-maintenance exercise/technique. Explain to your client:

> *"You see, dominant hands dominate our minds. The point of choice awareness is to free the mind from this kind of lateral domination. And we accomplish this by switching the hand you use while you eat."*

Encourage your client to use his or her non-dominant hand when eating to cope. This will make the episode of emotional eating more awkward and therefore mindful. After all, autopilots keep things smooth, don't they? So, awkwardness is a good thing, it calls on the mind to attend to what you are doing.

Eating with Atypical Utensils

Utensils provide utility. We are not interested in utility at this point. We are interested in awareness. Utility puts us to sleep. It's too familiar. We are interested in awkwardness. Awkwardness wakes us up and keeps us awake. Familiar utensils cue our hands and our minds into zombie eating. Unfamiliar utensils get in the way – in the way of our autopilot. Thus, the suggestion is simple:

> *"Use wrong utensils as an awareness-maintenance technique.*
> *Use chopsticks for eating grapes. Have a cup of chicken soup through*
> *a sipping straw."*

Encourage your client to throw a monkey wrench into their eating so as to keep his or her mind online during an emotional eating episode.

Reposition Your Body to Reposition Your Mind

Invite your client to change their eating posture: If they eat to cope in a rush by the refrigerator, have them sit down. If they eat to cope in their lounge chair in front of TV, have them sit on the floor or have them standing. Help your client see that changing bodily posture can serve as a powerful pattern-break to reposition one's mind – to shift it from the mindless familiarity to the unfamiliarity of mindfulness.

Relocate Your Body to Relocate Your Mind

Same goes for changing the setting: If all the emotional eating takes place in the kitchen, move it to the dining room. If it takes place in the bedroom, move it to the basement. Move the body to move the mind – or run the risk of having the mind remain stuck in its coordinate of mindlessness.

Coping With Eyes Closed

As an awareness-maintenance pattern-break, invite your client to eat with their eyes closed when they eat to cope. Explain:

> *"After your first course of relaxation, wake yourself up with a circle*
> *drawing exercise. Then get some comfort food and eat it with your*
> *eyes closed. Mindfulness is a different way of seeing: it sees even with*
> *the eyes closed. In fact, you might find out that mindfulness sees even*
> *better with the eyes closed. Try this pattern-break to see what it does*
> *for your mind."*

Exotic Appetizers

Comfort foods put us to sleep – if not literally, at least behaviorally. But familiarity is a foe of mindfulness. So, the suggestion here is to use an exotic food as an awareness appetizer and therefore as a way to maintain awareness. Explain to your client:

> "Listen, I know you like mashed potatoes (or chicken soup, or chocolate) for coping. And you are absolutely free to use these comfort foods. There is no reason not to. But here's what I suggest you try as part of your choice awareness training. Go out to Whole Foods or an ethnic grocery store and get a few unfamiliar foods. And you use them as choice awareness appetizers. So, after the first course of relaxation, after connecting to the body, wake your mind up – treat it to something new. Say, have some dried seaweed as a choice awareness appetizer. Chances are you won't know how to eat it. And that's good. That will force your mind to wake up and make some decisions. Do I fold it? Do I roll it? How long do I chew it? Shall I dip it into something? All these questions and the novelty of the taste itself is a pattern-break. It brings your mind online. And here's an important point: These choice awareness appetizers don't have to taste good; that's not the point: The point is to go off the autopilot to keep yourself off the autopilot. And then, once your mind is awake, you can have your comfort food for the rest of your mindful emotional eating episode."

This might or might not have an impact on the client. They might or might not appreciate this particular pattern-break. Worry not, clinician. You have many different options. Use these exercises as CAT homework, the more there is to try the more time your client is likely to spend in waking themselves up. And time is what assures the development of habit.

Key Points & Going Forward

There are two ways of proceeding in Session 2. If you are working with long-term context and can afford to take time, then you can devote the entire Session 2 to Relaxation Training. If, however, you are working with a shorter-term model and you are using MEE as a stand-alone intervention, then Session 2 must be divided in half between Relaxation Training and Choice Awareness/ Pattern Interruption Training.

Either way, Session 2 ought to begin with a few minutes of review. Recall that there was no homework after the first session. We simply left our clients in a kind of pleasant shock of not being judged. We left our clients to mull over this whole business of humanistic harm reduction. We gave them a lot to think about. And that was more than enough to get them started. Yet, it is still worth your clinical while to touch base with your client to see if the change in perspective on emotional eating changed the experience of emotional eating. But don't pause on this too long since you have a lot of skill-training to do in this second session.

In contrast to Session 1, Session 2 does come with homework. If Session 2 is solely devoted to relaxation training then your homework is focused solely on relaxation homework. If, however, you are using Session 2 to combine Relaxation Training and Choice Awareness/Pattern Interruption Training, then, naturally, your homework prescription is going to be more involved and…more integrated. I usually combine both Relaxation Training and Choice Awareness/Pattern Interruption Training into one session and I structure my homework Rx as follows:

> *"We've covered a lot of ground in the last couple of sessions. You've been introduced to a variety of relaxation quickies and to a bunch of pattern breaks. In the week to come, between now and the next session, your challenge is this: I'd like for you, whenever you can remember, to start each and every meal with a course of relaxation and with a course of choice awareness. Whether you are eating out of hunger, or because it's time to, or just snacking/grazing, or eating for emotional reasons, I'd like for you to start off with a 1-2 punch: first course – relaxation, second course – choice awareness. First, before you eat, connect to your body with a relaxation shortcut of your choice. Then, before you eat, connect to your mind with a circle drawing exercise. And then, if you are feeling particularly motivated, use some kind of pattern interruption trick to keep your mind awake while you eat. Now, I understand that you've got a lot going on and you might not always remember to do it all. It's natural if you feel like you don't want to mess with any of this during regular eating. But I do encourage you to stick to this 1-2 punch, to this mindful emotional meal 'architecture' whenever it comes down to emotional eating. Remember that our goal is not to eliminate it but to make it mindful. And that requires practice."*

Naturally, if you are devoting the entirety of Session 2 to Relaxation Training, then Choice Awareness/Pattern Interruption Training would have to wait till Session 3 at the end of which you'd encourage the client to continue to practice relaxation at the first course and then you would add Choice Awareness/Pattern Interruption homework on top of it.

The upside of combining Relaxation Training and Choice Awareness/ Pattern Interruption Training into one session is that your clinical homework introduces the client to a more integrated view of mindful emotional eating from the get go. This way, right off the bat, your client gets an unfragmented overview of how this new way of eating-to-cope mindfully would work. If, as a clinician, you are still unsure about how to clinically proceed, please, refer to Chapter 5 for more details on packaging these interventions and for the overview of the treatment flow.

Chapter 4 | Not Minding the Mind
(Craving Control Training)

It's the mind that carries us away into its own mindlessness. You start off mindfully and then something pops into your mind and off you go, on an autopilot, into a mindless nowhere. It's the same with eating in general and eating to cope. You start off mindfully: You relax, you wake up your mind, you work to keep it awake, then a thought pops into your mind that you wouldn't mind having some dessert on top of these mashed potatoes and then you mindlessly yield to this craving. Before you know it, what started off as a mindful emotional eating episode somehow grew into a run-away mindless binge. The challenge in front of us and in front of your client is to learn to not mind one's own craving mind. Put differently, this part of MEE is about *the elusive art of stopping.*

And this is pretty tricky business… You see, whenever you introduce a "should" into your mind, like a "you should stop eating now," you are introducing a source of resistance. A "should" divides us in two: the one eating and the one who is trying to stop the one eating from eating. Thus, a "should" creates friction, like the kind you hear when you slam on the brakes when speeding. And yet "shoulds" are necessary. You *should* stop eating at some point even if you are eating cope, shouldn't you?

Starting to eat to cope is easy. Stopping an emotional eating episode is a different story: It's much harder. Indeed, allowing yourself to take care of yourself by eating is like walking downhill. Feels effortless. But stopping and saying "enough" to yourself (which is code for "no") requires a good set of brakes lest you slide straight down into an uncontrolled mindless binge.

Question is "When to Stop?"

When it comes to plain eating, eating out of hunger, the stopping point is obvious. We – in the Wildly Overeating West – all know it even if many of us ignore it. You should stop when you are either no longer hungry or when you have reached a point of pleasant fullness. If you keep on eating beyond either of these points, you are overeating. We all know that and the fact that we don't heed our own advice speaks to the power of behavioral inertia: a body in motion, as the principle goes, stays in motion – unless it trips up over its own mind that is in the way.

Things get both murkier and harder when it comes to emotional eating. Emotional eating, in its pure form, is not about relieving the physiological hunger, but about relieving the emotional hunger. So, the rules of engagement are a bit different here. Emotional eating isn't about the physical fullness but, at a minimum, about emotional relief and, at a maximum, about hedonic pleasure. Thus, it'd make sense to stop emotional eating as soon as you are emotionally relieved, let alone when you are emotionally full. In parallel to the changes in the state of your mind, your body too is undergoing changes: it's getting fuller. First, it becomes pleasantly full and then unpleasantly full. Pleasant fullness would seem to be just the right time to bring the emotional eating episode to a pause, if not to a full stop. After all, to keep eating past the pleasant fullness is to negate whatever emotional gains you've experience up to this point.

To sum up, when it comes to mindful emotional eating, the two recommended stopping points are:

- as early as when you experience emotional relief (i.e. when you stop feeling bad)

- and no later than when you experience the onset of pleasant physical fullness (which, by definition, is accompanied by a sense of pleasure or satisfaction, which is tantamount to an emotional gain) (i.e. when you start feeling good)

Question is "How to Stop?"

Most emotional eaters claim to know exactly how to stop eating. But when you ask them about how they plan to stop eating what you get is something vacuous and circular along the lines of: "I just need to have a bite or two and then stop." There is no plan here, just a mere intention to invoke the magic of willpower. If you probe further into this non-plan you run into the same vacuous circularity: They will just… "will" themselves into self-control. This, of course, is psychologically naive. If willpower hasn't worked reliably in the past, why would it work reliably in the future? So, what is needed here is a serious discussion of how stopping works.

Letting Go of a Craving Begins With Letting a Craving Come

Metaphorically speaking, the main task of this step is to offer your client a method for developing a set of good behavioral brakes. We are talking about propping up the executive functions of the neocortex in its battle with the limbic (emotional) brain. Except that we are going to take the battle out of this battle. What we want to do is to equip your client with friction-less brakes. The idea is to teach your client how to win without fighting, how to stop eating without stopping oneself. Anything less than this will only add to the very stress that your client is trying to relieve through emotional eating. You see, the art of stopping is really the art of letting go (of a craving to continue). And the art of letting go of a craving to continue is the art of letting this craving come in the first place. In sum, we are talking about a kind of Gandhian approach to craving control in which you avoid a direct confrontation and instead resist peacefully. To clarify, the self-control strategy that I teach is not a form of emotional suppression. It's a form of metacognitive distancing. A form of mindfulness that is characterized by a fearless stance of witnessing your mind do what it does without doing anything about it. It's a form of mindful non-doing. A letting – a letting-come and a letting-go. It is a form of self-control in which you gain control by letting go of control.

This may sound paradoxical but that is exactly the paradox of this form of self-control. I've written about this method under the moniker of "dots and space," or "a riverbank attitude," a phrase from the writings of James Austin, the author of *Zen and the Brain*. Even though the technique is rooted in Eastern traditions, you don't have to be a Buddhist to learn it or use it: It's fun and value neutral and is almost offensively simple. You won't need to explain this paradox to your client. At least not just yet. This point is primarily for you, fellow clinician, to give you a sense of where we are going. The idea itself will become self-evident through the actual experiential practice.

Creating the Shared Narrative

In prepping up for the actual self-control training, work to create a shared base of terminology, a common narrative for discussing what it takes to stop eating. In particular, tell your clients that the self-control/craving-control method that you will teach them is not a matter of willpower but a matter of "skillpower." Skillpower is trainable. Willpower, as I see it, is not.

As part of developing a shared clinical narrative, begin to reframe self-control as impulse control and begin to use impulse control interchangeably with craving control. Explain that essentially any self-control is impulse control. Self-control is impulse management. Thus, self-control = impulse-control = craving-control.

And in our case, the impulses to manage are generally three-fold:

- a craving for something else to eat (a desire for a specific food)

- a desire to keep on eating just for the sake of eating (a desire for continued eating)

- an urge to release the self-monitoring tension of mindful emotional eating and to just shift into an uncontrolled mindless binge (a desire to numb out)

After presenting these different types of cravings and desires to manage, explain that the specific craving control method that you have up your sleeve is mindfulness-powered (I usually avoid the term "metacognition" but I use it here for the clinical reader). Emotional eating clients like the idea of systematic craving control. And that it comes with a method. They know they need to master this art of stopping and craving control training sounds like exactly the solution.

Metacognitive Distancing as Self-Control/Craving Control Training

Metacognitive distancing is when you are able to observe the various formations and manifestations of your mind without acting upon them behaviorally. If this sounds like a form of vispassana-style mindfulness, it's because it pretty much is. This kind of passive, non-reactive awareness feels like a distance from your own mind. And with this sense of distance comes a sense of control. Like a sense of control without controlling which is what I mean by "frictionless brakes" and "taking the battle out of the battle." It is exactly this kind of metacognitive stance that makes stopping possible without stopping. This curious state of mind allows you to watch your mind pass on its own, dissolve on its own, without you having to do anything about it.

So, instead of having to fight yourself and over-rule yourself and force yourself to stop eating, you simply let your desire to continue (eating) pass on its own. In effect, you stop eating without having to stop eating. Indeed, you stop eating because you have allowed a desire to keep on eating pass on its own. In sum, nothing is required of you but to watch the drama of your mind take care of itself. This method is grounded in the Buddhist psychology of anitya which means impermanence: Reality is fluid, everything passes on its own, thus, there is no need to force the flow of reality to pass, it'll pass on its own, if you know how to calmly wait while it does.

Method Specifics: "Dots & Spaces"

The best way to teach something is to first learn it yourself. So, let me present you with this method for cultivating metacognitive self-control as you would present it to your own client in the last session. In the next page or two, I'll be addressing you as if you were my client, and I invite you to not just read through this exercise, but engage in it as you go along, including following the instructions in brackets. Generally, it helps to use several stages to roll out the entire technique. The technique is assembled piece by piece, like a block tower. Each piece matters. The sequence of these pieces matters, too. Trying this out matters.

Step 1: Metaphor "Mind Is a River". You know how you have a thought and then something else pops into your mind? Or you have a feeling and you feel sort of caught up in it, but then it eventually passes? Well, that's the intriguing thing about the mind: It's kind of like a river. What makes a river a river is that it moves, it flows, it constantly changes, passes on. It's the same with our minds. When you look inside, when you start paying attention to your mind, you begin to notice that it's a continuous stream of experience. Sometimes, it feels like a thought; sometimes it feels like a feeling; sometimes it's an urge, a kind of itch to act, an impulse to say or do something. So, what I want you to do in a minute is to spend some time watching this river, watching this flow of experience. I call it "riverbank attitude." It's as if you are sitting on the bank of the river watching the water flow. You might see an empty soda bottle float by or a leaf or a duck—all these things come and go. That's the neat thing about a river: It takes care of its own garbage. You really don't have to do a thing—you just sit and watch your mind pass.

Step 2: Instruction "Dots". So, here's exactly what I want you to do. [Hand the client a stack of sticky notes and a pen.] I'd like you to sit back and watch this river of your mind for a little bit—maybe a couple of minutes—I'll stop you in a bit. What I want you to do is this: Each and every time your mind changes, put down a dot on a piece of paper. That's all. So, say you have a thought: "I don't understand what this is for." That's a thought—an event of your mind. Put down a dot and see what your mind does next. Let's say your next thought is "This is boring." or maybe, "This is interesting." Whatever it is, notice the thought pop into your mind, put down a dot and wait to see what happens next. You might have a feeling of restlessness, which might come up as a thought: "Has it been two minutes yet?" Notice the feeling and put down a dot. Notice the thought and put down a dot. As you see, the content of what you are experiencing here is sort of irrelevant. What matters is that you stay on this riverbank of your mind. Just keep noticing what occurs to you and put down a dot. Now, you don't have to catch each and every thought. This isn't about some kind of performance. Just catch what you can, dot it down, see what happens next. Go ahead, and I'll stop you in a moment.

—🎋 *Step 3: Processing.* [Ask the client (or yourself)] What was this exercise like for you? [The client might tell you, "I was surprised how many dots there were, how many thoughts there were..." Explain to the client] That's what happens when we stay put on that riverbank. Usually, we just get caught up in the river of experience, we get carried away and start acting on these thoughts and feelings. We get hijacked by a desire, by an impulse, by an urge, so to say. But here, you just stayed put on that riverbank.

—🎋 *Step 4: Instruction "Dots & Spaces".* Now, I'd like to add another piece. Whereas the first time you did the exercise, you began by noticing the thoughts and feelings that would pass through your mind, now I'd like you to begin by noticing the sensations of your breath. For example, just notice how your chest moves up and down as you inhale and exhale. So, in a moment, when you begin, I'd like you to start with this breath focus, with this breath awareness. Let this be the riverbank on which you sit—your home base, so to say—the gap in between the dots. And then, as soon as your mind distracts you from your breath with some kind of thought, dot it down and return to your breath. So, say you sit there paying attention to your breath and then you suddenly have a thought: "Oh, I get it. I see how this would work with anger," just jot down a dot and go back to your breath focus.

—🎋 *Step 5: Processing.* [Ask the client (or yourself)] What was that like? [You'll probably hear something like, "Hmm, there were far fewer dots ... I felt calmer. It was relaxing ... I am relaxed now." Tell the client] Good, seems like you are beginning to see how this is going to be useful to you.

—🎋 *Step 6: Instruction.* "Notice the Impulse": There is just a bit more for us to play with here. Let's do this again, but this time, I'd like for you to only jot down (dot down) any impulses you might have. For example, say you sit there paying attention to your breath and then all of a sudden, you feel like scratching your nose. That's an impulse. Put down a dot and then, if you still feel like it, scratch your nose. But first put down a dot. So, first you notice the impulse and then make a choice: To scratch or not to scratch. If you decide to scratch your nose, go ahead and do it and then return to your breath focus. Then, say, in a moment, as you are paying attention to your breath, you notice that you want to change your posture or that you want to close your eyes or that you want to open your eyes or that you want to move your head to look around or look at the clock or ask me if we are done yet. Whatever the impulse might be, just notice it first, put down a dot and then decide: to act or not to act. If you decide not to act, notice what happens to the urge—will it pass on its own without you acting on it? Or will it linger? If it lingers, dot it down again, and see if you want to act on it or not. If it passes or if you satisfy it with an action, then just return to your breath. You get the idea. So, I'll shut up now for a few minutes and let you play with this, and then we'll discuss it.

Step 7: Processing + Reframing the Lingo. [Ask the client (or yourself)] What was that like? [Address any confusion, repeat any parts of this exercise if necessary and process client's feelings and reactions to the exercise and any thoughts they might have about how this may come in handy.] Before we go on, let me explain why I've been using the term "impulse" in this context. You see, a craving is an impulse. A craving is an urge. And an urge is an impulse. A craving compels you, it prompts you and edges you on to act upon it. In our case, the craving to watch is the craving to keep on eating or the craving to shift to mindless eating or the craving to just say "forget it" and to go into mindless, uncontrolled, all-out binge-eating mode.

Step 8: Alternative Version Instruction "Taps & Spaces". Now, let's try an alternative version of this. I call it "taps and spaces." Here's what I'd like you to do. [Model as you speak] Put your hand down on your knee with your palm down, and instead of jotting down a dot, just use the tip of your index finger to ever so slightly press into your knee or thigh whenever you notice your mind move with emotion. So, in a moment when you start doing this, close your eyes and watch your breath, and whenever you get distracted with a thought or a feeling or an urge of some kind, just press (tap) your finger into your knee as if you are jotting down a dot. Try that.

Step 9: Processing. [Ask the client (or yourself)] How was that? How did this compare to "dots and spaces"? Which did you like more? [Process the experience and repeat if necessary.]

Step 10: Self-Control Homework. I think it'd be very useful if you could practice watching your mind like this. This will help you reinforce your sense of self-control. This will help you master the art of stopping by letting the desire to continue to come and go. More specifically, practice sitting on this riverbank for a few minutes: Watch your mind pass, notice thoughts come and go, notice feelings come and go, notice sensations come and go, notice urges and impulses and cravings come and go. Realize that you really need to do nothing but watch and witness your mind pass on its own. To recap, the technique that we worked on today is a kind of self-control by not controlling. It's a form of controlling by letting go. And the thing is that to let things go, you have to let them come first. So, as you sit there watching your breath, whatever arises, let it come, however disturbing or upsetting. Let the sensation arise, dot it down, or, if you are using the portable version of this, just dot it down with your finger and then watch it pass.

The most amazing thing about all of this is every thought or sensation or feeling or urge passes. Mind passes. River flows. Life changes. [Repeat with emphasis] I don't know if you caught this or not: Every thought or feeling or sensation or urge passed. It's a kind of catch-and-release form of self-control. It isn't about suppressing the urges and cravings. It's about simply noticing what happens inside of you from this riverbank of calmness. So, your only task is to sit and witness your mind pass on its own. Now, you might be motivated to go ahead and start using this technique to either stop your emotional eating episode in the first place or to stop from continuing whenever you feel a sense of emotional relief or a sense of fullness. You certainly can. But remember we are not trying to eliminate emotional eating episodes in the first place. What we want to do is to keep them mindful, keep them from becoming mindless run-away binge-eating. So, you'll need a good bit of practice in this technique. And with this in mind, it'll be helpful if you practice this method when you *don't* need it so you can more effectively use it when you *do* need it. Don't just save this up until your next emotional eating episode. Practice pumping these brakes beforehand.

Middle Ground: Craving Control in Moderation

Any good tool can be put to misguided use. Be clear with your client: This craving control training is not intended to be in the service of rigid abstinence from any and all emotional eating (it's not possible anyway). Clarify to your client that craving control is not meant here for eliminating/preventing emotional eating but is intended to make mindful emotional eating a viable and effective option. The very thrust of the current program is to allow emotional eating in moderation, to humanistically sanction it and to make it more effective by making it mindful.

At the same time we don't want to go to the other extreme, the extreme of full-time permissiveness and total non-resistance. In the spirit of middle-way harm reduction, it is a good idea not to always yield to what might be a very fleeting desire for emotional eating. So, one of the obvious applications of this self-control is craving-control on the front end of the potential emotional eating episode. Explain to your client that, as a matter of rule, when they develop a desire to eat to cope, it's recommended that they spend a few moments on the riverbank of metacognition. They just might find that the desire for emotional eating will pass, particularly, if they allow it to come. Remember to let go of something we have to first let it come. So, be clear:

> *"Just because you have a desire for emotional eating, just because you want to eat to cope, it doesn't mean that you automatically should. Take a few moments to sit on the riverbank of your mind to see if this desire passes. If it doesn't, if it lingers, then, of course, yes, you can proceed to a mindful emotional eating episode. But this way you will do so from a position of choice and you will stand a better chance of success than if you were to rush into mindful emotional eating on the first fleeting desire to eat to cope."*

The second major application of this kind of self-control is to keep an emotional eating episode from turning into an overeating episode or into a binge. After your first serving of comfort food of your choice or as soon as you begin to experience the onset of pleasant fullness or the emerging sense of emotional relief, hit the pause button and spend a few moments on this riverbank to see if you are feeling better and to see if there are any somatic signs that you should stop here. Look inside to notice any desire to keep on eating. Let such desire come and go. Dot the desire away, or tap it away. You might also have cravings for specific foods. Notice those thoughts come and go as you linger for a few more minutes on this riverbank of self-control. Dot down or tap down these food-specific cravings; let the river of the mind wash away its own desirous restlessness.

So, my point here (and the point you'd do well to make to your client) is that craving control can be used to prevent some of the emotional eating episodes and it can be used to assure that any and all of the emotional eating episodes do not decompensate into mindless binges. Whereas the prevention application of craving control is optional, the binge-prevention application of craving control is mandatory. To clarify, if your client wants to eat to cope, they may or may not use the riverbank attitude to check to see how fleeting of a desire it is. But if they have in fact decided to go ahead and eat to cope they should, as much as they can remember, use craving control know-how to try to bring an otherwise successful emotional eating episode to a stop at the onset of moderate fullness and/or when they feel the onset of emotional relief. At the risk of being redundant, let me express this yet another way: While your client doesn't always have to bother to prevent an emotional eating episode, they should always try to prevent a mindless binge.

Additional Self-Control/Craving-Control/
Impulse-Control Homework

There are many different ways to practice this kind of self-control. It makes sense to encourage your client to practice self-control right before any kind of eating, even if it is eating normally, out of hunger. Talk about the urgency of such a moment. Just say something along the following lines:

> *"You know how you get a little restless when you are really hungry? You can't wait to satisfy that hunger? Well, that's a perfect time to practice impulse control. Get the food ready and just sit there at the table for a couple of minutes with your eyes open. Notice the impulse to eat arise, dot it down or tap it down as you witness it, refocus on your breath and notice the impulse pass. What to do if the impulse doesn't pass? Just notice it change. Change is passing. Whether it's growing or subsiding, it's passing from one state to another. Just notice when it spikes, tap it down or dot it down to discharge the energy of the impulse and refocus on your breath. Those few minutes before you eat can be excellent impulse control practice. We usually eat several times a day, so combining impulse control training with eating is a great way to build this skills training opportunity into your daily routine.*
> *The same goes for wanting seconds or dessert. Notice the desire to have seconds, tap it down or dot it down, refocus on your breath and see if it passes. Same with dessert. Should you have seconds and/or dessert? That's not the point. Make a conscious choice. That, too, is part of anger management practice."*

We are restless creatures, so opportunities for self-control training are everywhere. Another simple homework idea is witnessing bodily restlessness and practicing impulse control. For example, invite your client to practice impulse control before sleep:

> *"You know how we all tend to toss and turn a little before we fall asleep? This is another excellent opportunity for you to practice impulse control. First, find a comfortable sleeping position. Then, whatever the position is, hold it for a while. So, if you are on your back with your hands along your sides, commit to this posture for at least a few minutes. Notice the impulse to shift your posture, to turn over, or whatnot. Tap it down and refocus on your breath. You just might fall asleep like that. But if you don't, you can, of course, change your posture in a few minutes. These few minutes of witnessing your impulses to turn from this*

riverbank of your mind are a great investment into your anger management skillpower. Remember, an impulse is an impulse is an impulse. As they say in yoga, stay in the asana that you are in. Any impulse you witness calmly is a step toward impulse control."

The same goes for other kinds of impulses, such as impulses to change channels on TV or to check email on your smart phone. The opportunities for self-control training homework are infinite and intriguing. A week worth of diligent practice is bound to leverage a good bit of efficacy about this elusive art of self-stopping.

Resting in Experiential Fullness

The point of emotional eating is to feel better or not to feel at all. The point of mindful emotional eating is to feel better. "Not to feel at all" is not an option. "Not to feel at all" is mindlessness, not mindfulness. This is the key difference between mindless emotional eating and mindful emotional eating. Explain this difference and then draw your client's attention to the word mindfulness itself. Break the word down: "mind-fulness." Say it with a pause: "mind [pause] fullness." Explain:

"There is a fullness that comes with mindfulness. An experiential fullness. I'd like for you to learn to rest in it. Let's do that 'dots and spaces' exercise again and this time I encourage you to take notice of that space of fullness in between the mind-events. Allow yourself to realize that when you are on that riverbank, somehow it's a place of contentedness, a place of 'enough-ness.' Play with that a little to see what I mean."

Process the experience. Reframe this "riverbank attitude" as a kind of experiential fullness.

Resting in Fullness Homework

Invite your client to "practice in fullness" during regular meals as well. The more precedents of restful self-control during eating – the better. It might be also great practice to have your client eat, say, a single serving package of M&M's® one at a time, while resting in fullness in between the pieces (any snack that we eat in small units – like potato chips or popcorn – would do). More specifically, invite your client to try eating a serving of piece-meal food by eating one piece at a time and tapping a way at least two impulses to put another snack-piece into his or her mouth before continuing, until the entire single-size serving is gone.

It is exactly these kinds of experiences that will help your client not only know how to stop an emotional eating episode from turning into a run-away binge, but to also dial up the experiential quality of emotional eating through savoring. Explain to your client that savoring requires time: It's hard to notice the taste when we are busy fishing out another cracker out of a bag.

Key Points & Going Forward

If you decided to fast-track the jumpstart, then your first session was about reframing the problem and reframing the solution. Your second session would have been split between Relaxation Training and Choice Awareness/Pattern Interruption Training. And your third session would have been entirely about Craving Control. If this is the track you are on, begin Session 3 with homework review (see Chapter 6 on how to do it in a manner that leverages rapport and compliance). Then, introduce the rationale for self-control/craving control training. Then demo it in session. Then prescribe the clinical homework. And finish up with previewing the final, 4th session of the fast-track intervention. Tell your client that in the last session you will be bringing it all together, packaging all these skills into one unified algorithm of mindful coping through eating.

If, however, you decided to devote your second session to Relaxation Training and your third session to Choice Awareness/Pattern Interruption, then the material of this chapter would play out in Session 4, with Session 5 being the wrap-up session. Whether you pull off this jumpstart in 4 meetings or 5 is fundamentally irrelevant. More time, of course, means more practice. But we don't always have more time. So, what's presented here is a maximally condensed version of this clinical curriculum. Back in your therapy room, pace yourself as you see fit, of course.

If there is one key point to reiterate to your client at the end of craving control training, it is this one: ***While it is in the nature of satisfaction to stop itself, craving control training helps.*** That's the short version. Here's the long version of this very important point:

> *"Satisfaction heralds cessation of what brings it about in the first place. Satisfaction is self-regulating. Eating is a perfect illustration of this self-regulation dynamic. Indeed, it takes eating to satisfy hunger. But as soon as this satisfaction is achieved, the onset of satisfaction puts a halt to any further eating. At least, that's how it was for all of us when we were kids and we ate intuitively. We needed no rules. We didn't have*

to remember to stop: fullness itself put a stop-gap on eating. But after years of ignoring our bodies, this self-regulating dynamic of satisfaction goes awry. Mindfulness works to restore this intuitive homeostatic dynamic. Taking time to rest in the fullness is literally a practice of satisfaction and contentedness; and therefore, a practice in the cessation of eating without the friction of having to fight yourself to stop eating."

Chapter 5 | Programmatic Notes: Packaging the Short-Term MEE Intervention

The last session (which might be your 4th or 5th depending on how fast you've been going) isn't just about review. It's about packaging all the skills together into a unified algorithm of mindful action, from start to finish. This last session is about crystallizing a humanistic harm reduction attitude and about setting up rules of engagement that will help your client turn their previously haphazard, guilt-ridden and mostly mindless emotional eating into a more effective ritual of self-care.

Packaging the Jumpstart

The short-term MEE intervention consists of an initial psychodydactic intervention (designed to reframe the problem of emotional eating and to reframe the solution in a harm reduction manner). The MEE jumpstart also consists of relaxation training, training in choice awareness & pattern interruption, and self-control training. Here's the recommended session-by-session breakdown of this material:

Session 1: Psychodydactic Intervention
Session 2: Relaxation Training + Choice Awareness Training
Session 3: Homework Review + Self-Control/Craving Control Training
Session 4: Homework Review + Overview + Rules of Engagement

For ideas on how to conduct humanistic, non-perfectionistic homework review see Chapter 6. Overview is an opportunity to recap the rationale behind the approach and to address any questions that your client might have about relaxation training, choice awareness/pattern interruption, and/or self-control training. "Rules of Engagement" is where you and your client work together to develop a step-by-step mindful emotional eating ritual, which is what the rest of this chapter is about.

MEE Rules of Engagement

Begin this last session of the short-term MEE intervention with the following set of principles for mindful emotional eating. Here is a set of modified and extended set of MEE principles originally described in *Eating the Moment* (Somov, 2008):

1. When eating to cope with emotions, accept emotional eating as a legitimate coping choice, not as a coping failure, and remember that that emotional eating does not have to mean emotional overeating.

2. When eating to cope, choose food that you want; indulge on quality so as to not indulge on quantity.

3. When eating to cope, eliminate distractions and follow a predictable MEE ritual, with clear start and end points.

4. When eating to cope, first activate the parasympathetic response through relaxation. Let relaxation be your first course.

5. When eating to cope, wake up your mind. Let choice awareness be your second course.

6. When eating to cope, keep your mind awake with the help of pattern interruption. Let mindful eating be your third course.

7. When eating to cope, keep track of any emerging sign of emotional relief and/or of any emerging sense of pleasant fullness.

8. When, as part of eating to cope, you have experienced a sense of emotional relief and/or a sense of emerging fullness, allow yourself to rest in the fullness of the moment using metacognitive distancing.

9. When, as part of eating to cope, you decided to go for seconds, repeat steps 4 through 8.

10. After eating to cope, regardless of the quantitative or qualitative outcome, accept emotional eating as a legitimate coping choice, not as a coping failure and congratulate yourself on yet another courageously attempted precedent of harm reduction self-care.

While some of these are relatively self-explanatory, some aren't and involve a certain degree of nuance. So, let us take a closer look at each of these principles. This will help prevent any possible misunderstanding between you, the reader, and I, and between you, the clinician, and your client.

Principle 1 - *When eating to cope with emotions, accept emotional eating as a legitimate coping choice, not as a coping failure, and remember that emotional eating does not have to mean emotional overeating.*

The idea here is to start an emotional eating episode on a note of humanistic harm reduction and with a clear intention of moderation.

Principle 2 - *When eating to cope, choose food that you want; indulge on quality so as to not indulge on quantity.*

Encourage your client not to skimp out on what they choose to eat when coping. Help your clients not fear their favorite foods. Explain that they stand a better chance of not overeating or shifting into a binge-mode if they allow themselves to have exactly the comfort foods that they crave.

Principle 3 - *When eating to cope, eliminate distractions and follow a predictable MEE ritual, with clear start and end points.*

Zen Buddhists say: *When you eat, eat.* I say: *When you cope, cope.* The point to highlight here is that distractions render mindful emotional eating mindless. Distractions – such as watching TV or reading or fooling around on your smart device – distract us from ourselves. The very point of mindful emotional eating is to tune in to ourselves, not to tune out. The old-school emotional eating of the mindless kind was, indeed, about tuning out, about forgetting self. Mindful emotional eating hangs a 180 U-turn here. The phenomenological vector of mindful emotional eating is self-remembering.

Principle 4 - *When eating to cope, first activate the parasympathetic response through relaxation. Let relaxation be your first course.*

This is pretty self-explanatory: Relax to reduce the amount of stress that you are planning to cope with by eating. Relaxation-as-the-first-course is the beginning of the MEE ritual. Review your client's relaxation options and ask them what specific relaxation technique they have found most useful. Encourage your client to begin to consider which particular "cocktail" of relaxation to commit to. The sooner they can choose the path that works for them the sooner they stand to benefit from conditioning and habit-formation.

—❧ *Principle 5* - *When eating to cope, wake up your mind. Let choice awareness be your second course.*

Choice awareness (such as "drawing a mindful circle") is the second course of a mindful emotional eating meal. Remind the client that after connecting to their body via relaxation the next step is to connect to their mind by waking it up.

—❧ *Principle 6* - *When eating to cope, keep your mind awake with the help of pattern interruption. Let mindful eating be your third course.*

The idea here is to use the pattern interruption techniques (such as "eating with non-dominant hand") as a way of keeping the mind on-line during the coping episode.

—❧ *Principle 7* - *When eating to cope, keep track of any emerging sign of emotional relief and/or of any emerging sense of pleasant fullness.*

Staying mindful during an emotional eating episode, with the help of pattern interruption, will help your client be mindful enough to notice any changes in their emotional or physical state. Remind the client of the necessity to pause as soon as they experience emerging emotional relief and/or pleasant fullness. Explain that eating beyond pleasant fullness will lead to unpleasant fullness and will therefore negate any emotional relief gained through emotional eating.

—❧ *Principle 8* - *When, as part of eating to cope, you have experienced a sense of emotional relief and/or a sense of emerging fullness, allow yourself to rest in the fullness of the moment using metacognitive distancing.*

This is a critical step. This is where the art of self-stopping comes in, that paradoxical art of coming to a stop without stopping yourself. Spend a good bit of time in highlighting this. Remind the client of how the "riverbank attitude" works. If necessary, walk them through it again. Help them see the subtle but essential distinction between forcing yourself to stop eating (which is stressful) and letting the desire to keep on eating (despite already feeling better and/or full) pass on its own. Principle 8 is a bookend piece for Principle 3: "Riverbank attitude" (craving control via metacognitive distancing) is that "clear-cut end point" of the MEE episode (except for when it isn't, which brings us to Principle 9).

Principle 9 - *When, as part of eating to cope, you decide to go for seconds, repeat steps 4 through 8.*

Help client to understand that if, after step 8 (the "riverbank pause") they decide to continue eating, they need to go through the same MEE ritual as they did in the beginning. Explain that doing so will help assure that Round 2 of MEE will not turn into an uncontrolled, mindless binge. Encourage the client to commit to having once again starting off with relaxation, then proceeding into choice awareness and then going into mindful eating proper with the help of pattern interruption, and continue to track for psycho-somatic changes, and stop for another "riverbank pause" no later than at the onset of unpleasant fullness.

Principle 10 - *After eating to cope, regardless of the quantitative or qualitative outcome of the emotional eating episode, accept emotional eating as a legitimate coping choice, not as a coping failure and congratulate yourself on yet another courageously attempted precedent of harm reduction self-care.*

The end of the MEE episode harkens back – attitudinally – to its beginning. This kind of circularity is intentional: You start with self-acceptance and you end with self-acceptance. Ending on a note of humanistic self-acceptance. More specifically, encourage your client to recognize that a) he or she has meant well (the motive was to cope and take care of oneself, not "to be bad" or "to self-destruct") and help your client recognize b) that he or she has done their coping best (see Part II for details on how to help your client leverage this kind of self-acceptance). It might also help here to introduce the following phrasing: "attempted precedent of mindful emotional eating." As in "Congratulate yourself on yet another attempted precedent of mindful emotional eating." As a clinician, make a note that what we are trying to do here is to channel Alan Marlatt's humanistic approach to relapse prevention here. The recognition of the partial success is quintessential decatastrophizing.

Mindful Emotional Eating Meal Architecture

In the wrap-up session of the MEE jumpstart it might be also helpful to talk about the "architecture" of the MEE meal. In a sense, it's just a recapping of the above points but through a slightly different lens. So, tell your client that from this point on you encourage them to think of the emotional eating meal as consisting of four courses:

- A course of relaxation
- A course of choice awareness
- A course of mindful eating ("powered" by pattern interruption)
- A riverbank pause of resting in fullness (as a form of craving control and self-stopping)

As you see, all we do here is that we sort the already established ideas and MEE lingo through a different metaphorical sift. This is a useful angle as we all have been programmed to think of a meal as consisting of various courses. Thus, it makes sense to capitalize on this course-based metaphor when it comes to planning a mindful emotional eating meal.

No Homework, Just Resources

Jumpstart is a stand-alone intervention. Thus, the last session of this short-term MEE intervention is possibly the end of treatment. Homework on the way out is bad clinical form. But a couple of sheets of paper might be a nice enough parting gift. While I am not a big fan of handouts in general, given the highly complex issue at hand, a summary of the key points of this intervention is value-added. With this in mind, I prepared a few simple MEE handouts for you to download. They are available to you on my book site (www.eatingthemoment.com) and at my practice site (www.drsomov.com).

Last Session is First Session

So, that's the short-term MEE intervention from start to finish. But the last session of this short-term approach to emotional eating is possibly the beginning of the long-term approach to managing emotional eating. There is more to do – there is the issue of binge-eating, there is more lapse/relapse prevention to do and a variety of other issues. In wrapping up the last session of the jumpstart, be clear about all of this with your client. Explain that they are off to a good start, that they now have a powerful set of skills. But there is still some tweaking to be done. And they don't have to do all of this at once. There is no need to communicate artificial urgency. Tell your client: "You have the rest of your life to work on this." And leave the door open for more.

Chapter 6 | Ego-friendly, Humanistic, Nonperfectionistic Homework Review

Clinical homework can be an iffy proposition. It can set up a teacher-student dynamic that can be counterproductive, particularly, if you, the clinician, get a little perfectionistic about homework compliance. Remember who you are working with: Many folks who come to you to work on eating issues can be pretty hard on themselves. What we want to avoid here is an all-or-nothing narrative of "failure v. success." So, you have to be careful not to be too pedantic or obsessive about the homework you prescribe. Thus, clinical homework review must be conducted with humanistic savvy. I recommend that you focus your homework review on the following four aspects of the change process:

- Precedents
- Trends
- Changes in self-view
- Behavioral outcomes

If you just focus on the outcomes you are running the risk of invalidating the effort. If the focus of your clinical attention implicitly communicates that all that matters is whether your client is eating emotionally less often and eating less, then you are inadvertently reinforcing client's own perfectionism and diet mentality. And that gets in the way of the change process.

Precedent Review

Precedent review is a kind of homework review in which all you are hoping for is a precedent of change. If such a precedent can be found, you make a point to celebrate it. You don't have to gush, but you do make a big enough deal about it to flag its importance for the client. When you do that, you create a non-perfectionistic attitude toward future homework. You are teaching the client that what matters is change – not accuracy, not precision, but change itself. And change begins with precedents. You know that whole point about how the journey of a thousand miles begins with one step? That's what I am talking about. Yes, it's a cliché, but it's a cliché that makes sense, and people recognize it. So, use it. Tell the client about the journey of a thousand miles and congratulate him or her on the first couple of steps taken.

Trend Review

Pay special attention to any emerging trends or a change of patterns in a client's behavior. Ask your client, "So, as you look back at the past couple of weeks since we started working on this, do you sense a trend emerging in how you use food for coping?" If the client recognizes any such trends, again, celebrate them. Make a big deal about them. But if not, reassure the client that his or her emotional eating habit has a lot of momentum behind it, and that it is entirely normal for this sort of thing to take some time. It's the process that matters. Also, pay close attention so as to not miss out on the new patterns and trends. Think of the stories you hear from the client, and see if you can connect a few stand-alone dots of precedents into a narrative of change that is gaining speed. Even if this trend is a stretch, it's a stretch in ego-syntonic direction, in a direction that supports change.

Self-View Changes

Ask the client how he or she has been feeling about himself or herself since he or she started working on making emotional eating more mindful. Has he or she been more at peace with himself or herself? Is the client feeling more in control? Has he or she been calmer? More balanced? More mindful? More present? And what's it like to discover that side of himself or herself? What's meaningful about that for the client? Has he or she had any epiphanies or realizations? Is the client more satisfied with his or her progress?

Behavioral Outcomes

The discussion of the actual behavioral outcomes should come last. It should take the back seat to the discussions of precedents, trends and changes in self-view. In fact, it is entirely ok to not even discuss the behavioral outcomes explicitly. As a clinician, it won't take much guesswork to see what is happening on the behavioral plane. Leave the initiative with the client: If they have something to share, to brag about, they will. And when they do, try not to overshoot and end up acting as if the outcomes don't matter at all. Of course, they do. That's what the client is there for. So, in dialing down the focus on outcomes, it is important not to ignore them. The rule of thumb here is to let your client bring up the issue of outcomes. At the same time, keep a close ear to what you are hearing about the outcomes. You just might need to revisit these emerging behavioral changes down the line should client's sense of efficacy lapse for some reason. As a clinician, you are not just a catalyst of change for your client but also a historian of their progress.

Orientation Towards Humanistic Change

Clinical homework review is not a scorecard or a weigh-in. There shouldn't be any make-it-or-break it feel about it. There are no tests to pass or fail. Nothing to prove or disprove. Just a project of change to allow to unfold. As I see it, humanistic homework *review* is a collaborative creation of a change narrative. Think about it: The goal of homework is indeed change, but the goal of homework review is not change per se, instead an attempt to leverage a healthy attitude with an orientation towards methodical but patient change. So, it really helps to communicate implicitly and explicitly that change is a process and that the client, in your opinion, is always doing his or her best. This attitude of unconditional acceptance matters: If the client feels your acceptance, he or she is likely to stick around, and then you can move him or her beyond the initial intervention (to Part II and III of this work) to talk more explicitly about an unconditional view of self which will serve as a powerful long-term relapse prevention strategy. So, here's some homework for you, the clinician: Dare to accept your client's homework outcomes. Whatever they might be.

Part II: Long Term MEE

Chapter 7 | Ordinary Perfection: Leveraging Self-Acceptance

By the time you are done with the first several sessions, your client will likely have come to appreciate your humanistic perspective on the issue of emotional eating. They will likely be surprised but they'll take it: They've come to you with a sense of shame and embarrassment, bracing for judgment, and they have been pleasantly surprised by the fact that you don't see their emotional eating as self-destructive. They will feel validated and finally seen. That's a good feeling. The challenge is to make sure that it doesn't just belong in this therapeutic relationship. The goal is to have your client internalize your compassion and acceptance for their struggle to cope effectively. Put differently, the challenge is to help your client internalize your acceptance of them as their own self-acceptance.

This is a tall clinical order and this is what this chapter is about. And I suggest that you tackle this explicitly instead of just waiting for this self-acceptance to come about naturally. It just might not on its own. Everything in our culture, in our civilization seems to conspire against self-acceptance. Self-acceptance doesn't sell jeans or cars. Self-acceptance is a form of social disobedience: a mind that is content makes for a lousy recreational shopper.

But, civic snark aside, let us get back to the clinical business of helping clients feel unconditionally accepting of themselves. This will help buffer your emotional eating client against future stress. Seen as such, this kind of clinical intervention that is designed to leverage self-acceptance isn't just a feel-good talk, but an essential relapse prevention measure and a form of strategic stress management (strategic stress management, by the way is when you position yourself philosophically in such a way so as to not sweat the proverbial small stuff; contrast this with tactical stress management – which is mindless emotional eating or mindful emotional eating or any other tactical coping choice).

Equation of Self-Acceptance

I like using equations for discussing the clinical variables that constitute a desired clinical outcome. There is just something self-evident in equations: They add up. So, without further ado here's an equation for leveraging self-acceptance:

$$\text{Self-Acceptance} = \text{Motivational Innocence} + \text{Effort Acceptance}$$

You'll see what this means as we go along. At this point my goal is to just introduce this conceptual schema and to encourage you to first engage your client in a kind of Socratic inquiry into what goes into self-acceptance. So, at some point, after the initial short-term MEE work, announce to your client that today, in this session, you want to spend a little bit of time on discussing self-acceptance. "What is this thing that people talk about? How does self-acceptance come about? How might it be useful to you as you work to fine-tune your coping repertoire?" That's it: Just nudge your client's mind, pop the questions, let your client think out loud and let them know that you have some ideas on how to go about trying to leverage it. And see if the client is game: Are they interested in continuing to talk about this in the sessions to come?

Motive Focus

Motive focus training begins with a discussion of what drives and motivates people. It's a theory-of-mind kind of discussion. As I see it, all human behavior breaks down to two elements of psychology: Motive and effort. Motive is universal: We are all pursuing well-being, moving from minus to plus, operating on what is known as the pleasure principle. The pleasure principle is not really hedonistic: It's about self-preservation, survival, and well-being. It is in this sense that we are all motivationally innocent, sinless. No evil here, no self-destruction either —we're just living, walking an infinite number of idiosyncratic roads to Rome.

As for the Socratic delivery of this point, it's pretty straightforward but impossible to script. It involves a discussion of what drives and motivates people. So, when you see the client beyond the jumpstart, just say:

> *"I want to talk to you about what drives and motivates us. You know, how we make sense of our behavior is really important. It makes a big difference in terms of whether we accept ourselves or reject ourselves.*

So, my question to you is, why do we do what we do? What makes
us tick? What's our motivational core? What do we want out of life?"

As you see, these questions are a bit leading, and that's fine. You are not
holding a philosophy class but a therapy session.

What is likely to eventually emerge from this discussion is the idea that
no matter what we do, our core motive is the pursuit of well-being. Whether
we eat to cope or don't eat to cope, whether we eat to cope in moderation or
binge eat, all we are really trying to do is to not hurt or to feel better. If you've
done a thorough enough job in Session 1 of the short-term MEE intervention,
your client already gets it. All you are doing here is extending this notion to
the broadest level of abstraction possible. The reason why has to do with why
the client eats to cope. A good bit of stress that the client deals with is self-
imposed – stemming from irrational guilt or shame or some sense of failure
or being self-destructive. By having such a philosophically-broad discussion of
what drives us and motivates us, you are trying to lead the client to conclude
that no matter what he or she does, at the core, he or she is just trying to avoid
pain or pursue pleasure. And that adds up to a sense of being motivationally
innocent. And that is the first big step to an unconditional acceptance of self.

In carrying out this discussion, think through a variety of possible
objections. For example, your client might struggle to see how it's all
fundamentally about pain and pleasure. They might say that we are guided
by meaning, purpose, love, faith, etc. Help them dig a little deeper. "Why
do we pursue meaning and purpose? Why do we love?" Once posed and
maintained, these kinds of questions inevitably lead you to conclude it feels
good to have meaning, that it feels good to love, that it feels good to have
the reassurance of faith, etc. Dare to dig deep within yourself to help your
client unearth their own motivational innocence behind all and anything that
they do. Stand firm on this: There is no evil, motivationally speaking, nor is
there any self-destructiveness. Heck, even an act of suicide is just a desperate
attempt not to be in pain, isn't it?

Be prepared that this discussion is not so much about the motivational
innocence that underlies emotional eating but about fundamental motivational
innocence that underlies all human behavior. Remember that you are not
working on emotional eating directly here but indirectly. You are trying to
help your client position themselves psychologically in such a way so as to
not have to rely on emotional eating for coping with the stress of self-loathing
and self-rejection.

Effort Acceptance

Rediscovering your motivational innocence takes you half-way to self-acceptance. The other part of this journey has to do with what I call "effort acceptance." Helping your client recognize that he or she is always doing her best will help reduce stress and self-doubt, and, most importantly, protect your emotional eating client from the self-deprecatory stupor of relapse.

Here's how you can go about leveraging effort acceptance. Start out by saying something along the following lines:

> *I want to make an argument to you that you are always doing your best. Are you interested in hearing it out?*

Most clients act surprised and intrigued. They hear something intuitively familiar in this proposition. I suspect we all already know that we are always doing our best. It's just that nobody ever dares to recognize this internal truth. It's hidden so deep that we ourselves forget it. So, when you roll out this premise, you know that the answer to your rhetorical question is going to be yes. Indeed, who wouldn't want to hear something like that about themselves?

If a client surprises you with a "no," then push the envelope a bit. Say: "Hear me out, would you? I do think that you'll find it of value. If nothing else, just for kicks, right? When will you ever have a chance to hear something as seemingly nonsensical as this, right?" Roll with the punches, be playful, don't give up.

And when you finally have their ear, continue:

> *"So, let's take this moment right now. You and I have been working on mindful emotional eating for a few sessions. At the beginning, you didn't know half of what you know now. But a time will come later when you will know more about mindful emotional eating than you know now. I want to talk about this moment right now though—not about the past or the future, but about this very moment in which you and I are talking. And I want to ask you a question: Can you now, at this moment, be any better at mindful emotional eating than you currently are?"*

Usually right away (but sometimes after a little bit of clarification), the client answers along the following lines: "No, right now I am doing the best that I can with what I know right now." If this is what you hear, then it's a slam dunk. The client has made the case for you. The rest is simple work of generalizing from this here-and-now truth to the rest of the client's life. After all, whatever is true now is always true, because all life is one lifelong now.

But sometimes the client says, "No, I could be doing better." If so, I follow up with, "So, you say that right now you could be doing better with emotional eating than you are doing, right? If so, then, why aren't you doing better than you are doing?" The client usually offers some kind of conditional clause, such as, "Well, if I were more choice aware, if I got better at stepping back from my craving thoughts..." What the client is doing is listing "ifs." But there are no "ifs" in reality. Reality is what it is. We might think in terms of "ifs," but there are no "ifs." Reality is all there is, from a moment to a moment to a moment. Helping the client to understand this helps counter his or her if-based thinking.

Continue to challenge:

"So, you are saying that if you invested more into mindful emotional eating practice, then you'd be better at it, right? (Client nods in affirmation.) But the thing is that all these "ifs" require time to come to life, right? (Client nods.) However, we aren't talking about how you are going to be at some point in the future; we are talking about how you are right now. Right now, as I see it, you are what you are. You know what you know. Your coping skill level right now is what it is. If it could be better right now than what it is, it wouldn't be what it is. But it is what it is, isn't it?"

Clinicians, fear not tautologies! And fear not circular reasoning. The tautology "it is what it is" is about as close as we come to truth without saying anything false. Truth—if there is such a thing-less thing—is in the center, and the best we can do is to circle around it in a dance of subjective interpretation. We are good at grasping the paradox of such self-referencing statements.

"In my experience, right at about this point of the exchange, the client starts getting it: "Yes, right now, I am doing the best that I can." Not yet fully realizing that all life is now, is in the now, the client cautiously emphasizes, "Yes, right now I am doing my best."

At this point say, "Ok, let's wait a minute. After a pause, I say "How about now? Can you be better right now at anger management than you are right now?" The light bulbs begin to go off. The client shakes his or her head and says, "No, not right now." After another moment, I say "How about now?" The client begins to smile. It's becoming self-evident that we are always doing the best that we can.

Summarize with the rhetorical question:

"So, when are you not doing your best? It seems that in whatever "now" I ask you this question, the answer would always have to be the same: You are always at your best, even if your best sucks in comparison to what you hoped for or planned for or in comparison to what had been expected of you by someone else. The point is that you are always doing your best, right?"

Once the client hears your parenthetical qualifier ("even if your best sucks"), he or she is really ready to fully internalize this idea. The hesitation is gone. The client now gets it that he or she has always done his or her best, is doing it now and will always do his or her best, exactly in proportion to the here- and-now variables at hand. Yes, his or her best might suck and fall short of his or her expectations, but the effort will always be at the maximum. After all, the universe cannot shortchange itself. It's not like some kind of celestial layaway is available in which the universe can save up its potential to do better and be better right now for some later point in time. And what is true for the universe as a whole is true for your client, who is a part of this universe. All that can be, is.

It All Adds Up

So, let us recap the emerging Equation of Self-Acceptance:

$$\text{Self-Acceptance} = \text{Motivational Innocence} + \text{Effort Acceptance}$$

You accomplish this powerful paradigm shift in self-view with the help of a Socratic dialogue and a bit of psychoeducation. This clinical intervention is quintessential philosophical counseling. It is an infusion of logotherapy into the behavioral nuts and bolts of this habit modification project. This isn't just a feel-good project. It's stress prevention. And, most importantly, it's a relapse prevention project.

If this process strikes you as a bit too heady, clinician, rush not to foreclose on it. You might be surprised by how effortless this really is. If you have done your job right so far (in other words, if you have managed to clinically sell the idea that emotional eating is not self-destructiveness but a form of intuitive self-care, if you have already communicated acceptance of client's effort through non-perfectionistic homework review), then you have already laid down a solid foundation for the client to finally internalize your acceptance of them as their own. In my experience, clients don't walk away from what feels good and makes sense. They might bristle a bit but a well planted seed of self-acceptance is bound to eventually burst into a blossom of well-being.

Chapter 8 | Serotonin of Impulse Control and Sweetening Willpower

No glucose, no willpower… When people have more demands for self-control in their daily lives, their hunger for sweets increases… The discovery of glucose effect does point to some useful techniques for self-control… Eat your way to willpower.

R. Baumeister & J. Tierney,
Willpower: Rediscovering the Greatest Human Strength

• • • • • • •

So, I am sitting in my home-base coffee shop on the charming South Side of Pittsburgh, with my well-lit laptop, working on this very book, in fact, typing these very words and I am not alone. I am in the company of a still virgin venti caramel macchiato (with extra whipped cream) and a white chocolate macadamia nut blondie. This gives you a very good idea of how I feel about this moment: I like reading books a lot more than I like writing them. Had I been sitting here with a book I want to read rather than with a book I have to write, I'd be quite content with a short cup of green tea with nothing more than a drop of half-and-half. But I am on a deadline, writing yet another book on mindful eating, so I have to figure out how to sweeten the deal a bit. Literally. You see, as Roy Baumeister has been reminding us over the years, self-control runs on glucose. "No glucose," he says, "no willpower."

Ego Depletion

As I look around this coffee shop with its cozy, well-appointed interior I see the demise of the institution of the library. It's not the Internet or the smart phones or the notion that people are reading less that is to blame for the much reduced library patronage. It's the old puritanical ban on food and drinks. For centuries people have gone to libraries for two reasons: to read for pleasure and to read to study. The former (pleasure readers) still frequent libraries; for them reading is voluntary and as such is sweet in and of itself. But for the latter – for those who have to read so as to study – the tedium of compulsory reading is better tolerated with a cookie in hand.

Point is: ego depletion (such as when you are faced with a difficult task of, say, staying on a diet or studying for a test) erodes self-control. Doing things that you don't want to be doing, such as resisting temptations and forcing yourself to abstain from a given behavior, is an energy-intensive proposition for your brain. To stay on task, to stick to the agenda, to remain with one's self-imposed parameters of behavior, brain requires fuel.

Neuro Catch-22

So, what does all of this have to do with emotional eating? Mindful emotional eating is emotional eating in mindful moderation. Mindful moderation involves heightened self-awareness, choice awareness, ongoing self-monitoring, self-control, impulse control and self-restrain. All of this places a great executive demand on your already fried brain. All of this neurological "have-to" is work and requires fuel.

So what we've got here is a neuro catch-22. Here's how Roy Baumeister and John Tierney explain this: "As the body uses glucose during self-control, it starts to crave sweet things to eat – which is bad news for people hoping to use their self-control to avoid sweets." Indeed, it would seem that in order to shift from mindless emotional eating to mindful emotional eating you need more mind. But more mind requires more fuel. Here's an all too familiar emotional eating scenario of the evening kind: It's late, you are fried (ego depleted) after a long day, all you wanna do is just veg a little and go to sleep. But you are trying to "be good" which you define as "not eating junk" and/or as "not getting stuffed." So, here you are doing your best trying to stay away from that bag of cookies that's been serenading you all day long, craving the very sweets that your brain needs to stay away from the very sweets you are craving. Circularity anyone? What a cruel paradox of nature, it seems.

Dare to Replete Your Ego

But we don't have to despair. The bad news here can actually be the good news. Here's a paradigm-shifting suggestion for you to try: Once you have made a conscious choice to cope by eating mindfully, you might as well combine the power of mindfulness with the power of glucose. How? By starting with dessert. You see, most of the time we don't dare to indulge. Instead, we tiptoe around our desires. We sheepishly pull the punch on self-care. We know what we want but we are too guilt-ridden to shamelessly go right after the object of our desire. What we want are the leftovers of that Ultimate Red Velvet cheesecake from the Cheesecake Factory® but instead we try to stuff ourselves with some puny baby carrots…only to eventually experience that "forget it." moment and end up inhaling everything in sight. Realize that a mindful emotional eating intervention that begins as a compromise tends to end as an all-out binge. The point is simple: Compromise not. Dare to replete your ego the quick way. Have the courage to give yourself exactly what you want from the very start or run the risk of facing a growing, ego-eroding tug-of-war of temptation after each and every tasteless baby carrot that you gag yourself with.

Stop teasing yourself, particularly, when you are at your most vulnerable. Recall: You are fried, you are beat, you want a moment of self-care, a moment of guilt-free indulgence so that you can call this mess of a day "a day" and move on. And yet, having given yourself the overall permission to cope by eating, now you are pinching caloric pennies like a granny at a penny slot machine, bit by bit blowing her entire stack without realizing it. You stand a far better chance of having a successful emotional eating episode, without getting carried away, if you go straight for the prize. Start with dessert and end with dessert, if it's the dessert you want. Spare yourself the frustration of self-patronizing; after all, the very point of emotional eating is to feel better quickly after an otherwise frustrating day, not to keep thwarting yourself any further. Remind yourself that emotional eating is meant as a coping shortcut – why take yourself on torturous detours of self-denial?

So, start your mindful emotional eating episode with dessert (if it's the dessert you want) and your brain will thank you. If it's the sense of self-control you yearn for, then make it nutritionally possible. Mindful self-indulgence in moderation is your best defense against temptation and an eventual loss of self-control – both psychologically and neuro-chemically. Remember "no glucose, no willpower," as Baumeister puts it.

Permission to Be in Control

We typically think of emotional eating as a permission to lose control. There is much to be said about this way of thinking: There is a kind of Dionysian release in this. By allowing yourself to get wild and not care, you relax. And that is the magic of mindless emotional eating. The magic of mindful emotional eating is different: It has to do with permission to be in control while you cope by eating. And this permission begins with a decision to indulge on exactly what you want. Baumeister and Tierney write: "Even just expecting to have to exert self-control seems to make people hungry for sweet foods"

(p. 51, 2011). That's right, many emotional eaters who are operating on the abstinence paradigm dread coming home, dread evenings, dread being in the kitchen because they expect themselves to be good, to not cope by eating. Naturally, this expectation of self-control, this mindset of abstinence becomes yet another stressor, often a chronic one at that. What we, as clinicians, and we, as eaters, want to do here is to change the paradigm: Give yourself and your clients the permission to have a taste of life's sweetness any time you want. Furthermore, when working on making your emotional eating more mindful and more effective, rethink your take on it – instead of thinking of emotional eating as a loss of control allow yourself to think of it as a form of self-control.

The More You Indulge, The More In Control You Are

Baumeister and Tierney describe the so-called German beeper study on resisting temptation. The results are fascinating: "The more willpower people expended, the more likely they became to yield to the next temptation that came along... the researchers were surprised to find that people with strong self-control spent less time resisting desires than other people did" (p. 33-239, 2011). Meaning: The more you resist, the weaker you get. The best way to win the tug of war with desire is either let it come and let it pass (witnessing it from a metacognitive distance, the so-called "riverbank attitude") or to choose to give in to it. A choice to give in to a desire is not a surrender but an act of self-control. It is exactly the conscious nature of such choice to give in that makes self-control possible. You are not being mindlessly stimulus-bound, you are not being high-jacked. You are mindfully acknowledging a stimulus and choosing a conscious response to it.

A "Yes" To Self is More Sustaining Than a "No"

Each time you choose a baby carrot instead of a bite of carrot cake (unless you are fanatical about baby carrots for some reason) you are saying a "no" to yourself. Each "no" to yourself dis-empowers you, weakens you. So, by the time you get through that proverbial bag of baby carrots you've depleted yourself and now you stand naked and vulnerable in front of the power-call of the carrot cake, with no self-control left to resist. Saying "yes" to yourself, saying "yes" to a bite of carrot cake empowers you, fortifies your ego and allows you to resist the rest of the carrot cake in the fridge. Instead of plowing through a boring bag of carrot sticks and then having the entire carrot cake, you have a mindful bite or two of the carrot cake, maybe even a slice and you are done, without having to raid the rest of your pantry in a "forget it." state of abandon.

So, How Would This Work in Real Life?

Here's the simple sequence for you to envision:

- You made a conscious choice to cope by eating mindfully
- You decided to fearlessly have exactly what you crave
- You first wake yourself up, with a Choice Awareness exercise (e.g., drawing a circle)
- You then relax yourself with a couple of moments of breath focus
- You then proceed to have a mindful or two of whatever it is that you crave the most, keeping your mind off the autopilot with the help of pattern interruption (e.g. using your non-dominant hand or wrong utensils to eat)
- You leverage maximum satisfaction through mindful savoring
- You pause to check to see if you have attained the emotional outcome you were hoping for
- If not, you take another moment or two to relax yourself a little more with breath focus and/or nasal breathing and allow yourself to mindfully continue to cope by eating
- After having attained a sense of emotional release, you congratulate yourself on a successful mindful emotional eating episode and on avoiding a binge (instead of beating yourself up for emotional eating)
- If, however, your mindful emotional eating episode decompensated into a mindless binge, do acknowledge the partial success of this coping moment: allow yourself to acknowledge that you a) meant well (that you were simply trying to feel better), b) that you did the best you could (given your current level of mastery with this style of coping), and c) that you did set a precedent (or yet another precedent) of approaching emotional eating methodically and with self-compassion; a partial success is still a success worthy of notice and satisfaction.

Tap the Placebo

So, the idea is quite straightforward: To restate Baumeister – no glucose, no mindfulness-powered impulse control. Or, no glucose, no mindfulness. But, of course, reality is a bit more nuanced than such a simple proposition.

Mindfulness and self-control is possible both on an empty stomach and with nothing more than a promise of sweetness. That's right, hope itself is sweet. The mere anticipation of self-indulgence is sweet enough. What you and your client are likely to discover is that when you allow yourself the permission to cope by eating, the tension is instantly released. And, when you allow yourself to avoid the hassle of eating a bag of carrot sticks and to indulge in exactly what you want, the release of that tension is even more profound. Think of this as the placebo power of emotional eating. So, tap it and see what happens. Next time you find yourself in a coping pinch (too late to exercise, your partner is too deep asleep to be of any support, that sort of thing), say hi to your sweet tooth. Get that little tub of ice cream out and put it on the counter top. Sit down, close your eyes, reset, relax, awaken and appreciate the sweetness of this moment: You are not afraid of self-care, you are done compromising for the day, you are free to have that "as-seen-on-TV" foodgasm moment. And you just might discover that you don't need it. But if you still do, indulge yourself – without shame, without guilt – and remember that a self-indulgence is self-sustaining.

Shortcuts and Detours of Satiety

Sugar is a hit from a crack-pipe. A bowl of rice, a protein bar – same hit but through a mile-long crack-pipe. Point is: Any food is glucose. Your brain doesn't really experience sugar per se – a curious fact in and of itself, right? Your body converts whatever you eat into glucose and converts glucose into a corresponding neurotransmitter. Different foods have different metabolic speeds. A sugary drink is a shortcut, a protein shake is a bit of a detour to the satiety of self-control. But it all works. And given the fact that you are in no rush, a low glycemic foodstuff would be just right as you spend a few moments on relaxing and awakening yourself. Once the permission to cope by eating is in, you have all the time in the world, the urgency is gone. So you are perfectly positioned to take your time with a low glycemic, body-friendly nutritional detour.

Harm Reducing Brain Candy

What we've learned from Baumeister & Co. so far is that glucose is willpower, i.e. self-control and, thus, impulse-control. What we haven't learned but do stand to experiment with is the range of actionable options. Question is: would it help to chew sugar-free gum right before you sat down to have a mindful emotional eating episode? I suspect that it might: A taste of sugar can be just satisfying enough to be self-sustaining. Why not invite your client to try it out, particularly, the calorie-shy client. Same goes for such calorically innocent interventions as a sublingual vitamin supplement (such as B-12, for example) or a sugar-free lozenge. Imagine combining first course of relaxation with a kind of frontal-lobe/executive-center priming of having something sweet dissolve in your mouth.

Case in point: For years I'd now and then sit down to meditate with a B-12 sublingual lozenge in my mouth. I liked the concept of it: B-12 came to mean "just being x 12 minutes." A lozenge would become a natural focal point, a slowly dissolving gustatory stimulus, a metaphor of impermanence. It also served as a timing device. So, imagine yourself as well, deciding at the end of a long day to cope via mindful eating. And with this compassionate permission to self to indulge, without any rush, you'd start out with the first course of relaxation, just as we have previously discussed, except that you'd also put a tiny red pellet of sublingual B-12 under your tongue and resolve to stay on the river bank of your consciousness while the supplement pellet dissolves. Now, I am not an M.D. or a nutritionist: I am not prescribing anything. I am just making a point. If you already take any kind of sublingual supplement, such as B-12 or vitamin D, then you might as well incorporate this moment of self-care into your decision to cope by eating mindfully. Seems intuitive, doesn't it?

Of course, it doesn't have to be a sublingual supplement of any kind, it can just be a piece of candy. Brain candy, so to say, for impulse control. Anything would do – anything that melts on its own, anything that can be consumed without eating, anything that dissolves. A square of chocolate is a great mindfulness-priming, focusing device. Take a moment to envision this powerful metamorphosis, what used to be a guilty pleasure with an accompanying sense of loss of control is now positioned to be the very vehicle of self-control – a smart way to turbo-charge your brain's willpower. Indeed, if you start off your mindful emotional eating episode with a course of mindful chocolate savoring, that Hershey's® kiss slow-melting under the observant stare of your mind's eye just might end up being all the emotional eating that you need on a given night. Come to think of it this moment of consumption approximates mindful non-eating: After all, the tiny dose of sweetness in your mouth dissolves on its own, much like most of the stress that plagues us. What a delicious shortcut to willpower and impulse control.

Courage to Encourage

It is essential that you understand the point of this chapter and that you help your client face the paradox of it all. Fear of change is normal. As a clinician, you'll have to bring the courage to encourage. It is up to you, clinician, to offer a steady enough IV of compassion and acceptance to help your client dare to experiment with shifting the paradigm. The change, once attempted, is sweet. As for my caramel macchiato and that macadamia nut blondie, here it is, still mostly untapped, sitting next to my laptop, as I am wrapping up this chapter. I've taken a few mindless and mindful sips of the drink. I've taken a few mindful and mindless bites of the pastry. The food has played its placebo role, it allowed me to settle in for a couple of hours of writing, it sweetened the moment, allowing me to move on from a "have-to-write" mode to a "want-to-write" mode. The magic of self-control in its ordinary perfection.

Chapter 9 | Sublimating the Binge Eating/Self-Restricting Roller Coaster

Transform urges to binge with conscious decisions to overeat. When you make a conscious decision to eat, or even overeat, you are not bingeing.
Linda Craighead, *The Appetite Awareness Workbook*

• • • • • • •

Clients and clinicians fear different things about my approach to emotional eating. Clients fear self-acceptance and clinicians fear compassion. Clients fear that self-acceptance will mean surrender and giving up and the end of change. And clinicians fear that their unconditional compassion and validation may boomerang as enabling and as a failure to encourage change. I can argue about that all day till my face is blue but at the end of the day the only thing that will truly convince you – whether you are my client or a fellow clinician – is your own experience. You don't have to take anything I propose on faith – field-test it and then learn from your own experience. And know all along that your fear and skepticism is entirely normal. But you will have to brace a little extra for what's coming in this chapter. The following approach to dealing with binge eating will scare the bejeebers out of you, because this approach to the binge-eating roller coaster not only involves a form of clinical doing but also a form of clinical non-doing. And as clinicians, we are ever more afraid of doing nothing even if this kind of non-doing is a way of reducing harm.

Defining a Binge

Differentiating a binge from emotional eating or emotional overeating is hard and simple. Hard if you go a quantitative route, if you count calories. Easy if you go a qualitative route, if you factor in the emotional mandate of these two types of eating. I'll take the easy path here. The subjective goal of emotional eating is to feel better. The subjective goal of binge eating is not to feel at all (i.e. to numb out, to disassociate somewhat or entirely). What this means is that binge-eating cannot be made mindful. Binge eating is a desire for mindlessness.

Another aspect of binge-eating that might or might not be generally true, but usually is, is that binge eaters are at least partial restrictors. What this means is that they try to compensate for overeating by undereating. In this they begin to approximate the dynamics of bulimia, minus such explicit compensatory behaviors such as purging, over-exercising, or using laxatives. This compensatory tendency of binge-eaters will come in handy when we try to sublimate this eating roller-coaster. You'll just have to read on to get a better sense of what I mean by "handy."

Three Approaches to Managing Binge-Eating

There are three ways to go here. One is common but impotent – that is an advice of abstinence. The second one is much less common – it's an approach of harm reduction. Think of it as down-shifting a binge to plain ol' emotional overeating. It involves a conscious choice to do so. Linda Craighead talks about it in her *Appetite Awareness Workbook* (2006). I talked about it in *Eating the Moment* (2008), too. The third approach is essentially unknown – it's a path of sublimation. Which is what this chapter is about. So, read on.

Clinical Non-Doing & Attitudinal Harm Reduction

Sometimes clients are ready to change and sometimes they are not. When clients are ready to change, you help them change. When clients are not ready to change, you try to see if you can help them become ready to change and if they do become ready to change, then you help with the change. But sometimes, and not infrequently, you have a client who is not interested in change. Period. Despite your best motivational enhancement efforts. As the wise minds of Motivational Interviewing tell us, we have to meet clients where they are. And sometimes we have to stay and work with clients where they are. So, if the behavioral change is out of the question, the only thing left to do is to help the client change how they feel about their behavioral patterns. And that is the art of clinical non-doing – it's attitudinal harm reduction.

Attitudinal harm reduction without a corresponding behavior change scares clinicians. Clinicians, particularly in this day and age of behavioral outcomes, have come to equate their clinical potency with behavioral changes. That is myopic: A change of attitude, while invisible, is an entirely acceptable existential outcome of psychotherapy. If your binge-eating client can shift from feeling ashamed and embarrassed about her eating pattern, she is now psychologically healthier even if she continues to remain at risk physiologically (which, by the way, is also debatable – I'll get to that in a few moments). Self-acceptance, as I see it, is not just a "good enough" outcome but an essential outcome of a successful clinical intervention. And there is nothing like humanistic harm reduction to leverage self-acceptance, particularly, with the binge eating population.

Chemical Alchemy of Sublimation

But we are not going to stop at helping our clients accept what is, as strategically useful as it may be. We can offer them a blasphemous solution – a solution that involves a permission to binge. That's right, not the kind of gear-downing, harm-reduction permission that Linda Craighead talks about when she talks about a conscious decision to overeat instead of bingeing. I am talking about an actual permission to binge eat. "On what basis?" you might ask. "On the basis of sublimation," would be my answer. Let me explain.

An old mentor of mine once defined sublimation as "turning s*!# into gold." If this strikes you as mildly pathologizing it's because it is. I prefer to define sublimation as "clinical alchemy" – as a process of turning something that is problematic into something that is less problematic. Viewed as such, sublimation is quintessential harm reduction. Sublimation as a clinical direction scares the clinician because, once again, it seems like clinical non-doing. As a clinician, you are not fostering any behavioral outcomes, just attitudinal changes. And somehow it just doesn't seem enough to you. But to your client, it's plenty. An attitudinal change makes all the difference for your client; not judging themselves, not feeling irrational, or not having to hide feels great. And this gain of self-acceptance, of course paves the way for an eventual behavioral change down the line. But sometimes it doesn't. Sometimes clients stay behaviorally exactly where they are for a very long time, if not for good. In such cases, attitude change is as good as it gets and to my clinical mind, that is plenty. You'll see why soon enough.

Two Kinds of Binge Eaters

There are two kinds of binge-eaters – those who want to stop binge-eating and those who absolutely don't. The latter category involves bulimic-grade devotees of binge eating – a sub-population that absolutely and categorically doesn't like being told what to do, a population that will keep on doing what they've been doing. Period. It takes us a while to realize when we run into this kind of wall. But once we do, we can either give up or we can recalibrate. The sublimation strategy is that kind of recalibration. Bear with me – we are almost to the meat of the matter.

Binge-Eaters Who Want to Change

The first sub-population – binge-eaters who want to stop binge-eating – is pretty straightforward. These are clients with motivation to change and with adequate ego resources to carry out their change agenda. My approach with them is a kind of down-shifting into mindful emotional eating and then, by way of diversifying their coping options, into a life of coping that does not solely rely on emotional eating. I take these folks on a 2-step journey: First, I help them down-shift their binge-eating into mindful emotional eating and then I help them shift from just food-based coping to non-food-based coping. So, initially, these binge-eaters regain a sense of self-control by switching to mindful emotional eating (with its choice awareness, emotional self-regulation and process mindfulness). And then, these folks begin to broaden their coping repertoire to include ways of coping that do not involve eating. In time, binge-eating itself disappears and what emerges instead is a life of eclectic coping in which sometimes you cope by going out for a walk and sometimes you cope by going out to eat. As you see, this is clearly a form of clinical doing, an active behavior-change intervention.

Binge-Eaters Who Don't Want to Change

Let's face it – not all clients want to change. Some, with elegant vehemence, will trump any argument for change with a brilliant counterpoint for keeping the status quo. So, what shall you do here – try to squeeze water out of a stone? Sure, you can refer them out. Or, if you dare, you can offer them attitudinal harm reduction, a path of sublimation.

What scares clinicians often pleases clients. While we fear that our humanistic validation will enable our client's so called "self-destructive" behaviors, our incalcitrant clients yearn for acceptance and for some clinically tactful tweaking of how to get along with the world that doesn't accept their eating style and their coping choices. Numbing out works for them and they wonder, after all the therapists that they have fired along the way, if you would surprise them with some kind of solution.

With such clients, I take the tact of clinical non-doing, i.e. attitudinal harm reduction, a.k.a. sublimation. I am not interested in a power struggle with them: To win such a struggle is to dis-empower them. I see no clinical value in that. I don't need to be right. I don't want to moralize and convince them that they are being self-destructive. To do so would be a violation of samma vacca, a violation of clinical "right speech." I don't want to be divisive with them. I am not interested in fragmenting their egos. Bottom-line: with clients like that my goal is to help them feel ok about binge-eating. If this smacks of enabling it's because it is: I am trying to enable self-acceptance as a kind of long-term clinical investment that may or may not one day pay off with behavioral changes. My default way of helping these clients feel ok is to leverage self-acceptance; you mean well + you are doing the best that you can.

"Obviously, what you feel is unacceptable to you. It's too much. You need to numb out. And you found a way to do it without getting into booze or drugs. I get it. It works well enough. At least for now." – is what I end up saying here. But I don't stop here...

Two Sublimation Vectors

Recall that sublimation is not behavioral change but attitudinal change (that may or may not lead to behavioral changes). The goal of humanistic sublimation is attitude change and, thus, a change in self-view. I use two sublimation vectors when working with binge eaters who don't want to stop binge-eating. The first is by now all too familiar for you, it's the idea of self-care. I reframe binge eating just like I reframe emotional eating, as a form of self-care, as a means of emotional self-regulation (see Chapter 1 for details).

The second sublimation vector is the idea of *intermittent fasting*. I reframe the binge-eating-self-restricting roller coaster as a form of intuitive intermittent fasting. In doing so, my client and I take the pseudo-sin of self-destructiveness out of binge eating and self-restricting. This positions the client to shift from self-loathing to self-acceptance and to also see the serendipitous method behind the apparent binge-eating/self-restricting madness. Suddenly, the client who felt chronically stuck finds oneself at the cutting edge of nutritional science on extending health span via calorie restriction. The shame is gone in a flash. The defensive bracing for social judgment has vanished. Instead, the client experiences a moment of righteous vindication: She feels that all along she must have been onto something, onto something intuitive, onto something that not only makes emotionally pragmatic sense but might even be physiologically healthy. It's a pleasant shock, a whopper of good news, a major glimpse of hope. The client feels smart and encouraged and suddenly open to fine-tune their binge-eating behavior to transform it into the cutting edge paradigm shift of health maintenance.

And this is where things get a little psycho-educational. To pull off this sublimation vector you need to do some homework on calorie restriction and intermittent fasting. Here's a brief review of relevant terminology to get you started but you will need to do your own research. Check out the references and stay on top of this evolving literature. Why? Because science is an evolving project, paradigms constantly shift. At the time of writing this book, this sublimation vector seems to enjoy empirical support but facts may change and if they do, you will need to rethink the appropriateness of this attitudinal harm reduction. Before we move on, let me be crystal clear on this point: The following suggestions are time-specific, reflecting the current realities of what we know. If the paradigm shifts again and we discover that calorie restriction and intermittent fasting are bunk, I'll be the first one to slam on the brakes and go back to my clinical drawing board in search of another sublimation vector. But as the facts stand right now, sublimating binge-eating and self-restricting into calorie restriction and intermittent fasting makes sense.

Fund of Knowledge: CR, F, IF, ADF, MF

What follows is an amateur overview of relevant terminology. While, as psychotherapists, counselors, social workers, and psychologists, we have the credentials to offer information towards attitude change and behavior change, we do not have the credentials to suggest diets. So, take what follows as the most cursory introduction to the emerging body of literature on calorie restriction and intermittent fasting. I'll make it quick and sweet: First, the knowledge base, then the actual harm reduction clinical "sales pitch."

CR: Calorie Restriction

Calorie restriction is just what the name suggests: a reduction of food intake. The Caloric Restriction movement (Delaney & Walford, 2010) didn't begin as a weight loss scheme but as an attempt to extend human life span and health span. The research on animal models has demonstrated that a certain percentage of calorie restriction can help stabilize health and prolong life.

F: Fasting

Fasting is going without food. We do it all the time – in between meals. Each night we go to bed and don't eat until we wake up at which point we break the 8 hour long fast with break-fast. Sounds familiar?

IF: Intermittent Fasting

True fasting is complete and total abstinence from food, for a period that is longer than the time between any two typical mealtimes. The "fasting" of the Intermittent Fasting movement varies from true fasting (say for 24 hours) to a partial calorie restriction (e.g. skipping one meal or having no more than one meal a day).

ADF: Alternative Day Fasting

Alternative Day Fasting is just that: you eat normal on one day and you don't eat at all on the day that follows. A variation on the theme might be: eating normal one day, and eating only one meal the following day.

MF: Modified Fasting

Modified fasting is again not true fasting but calorie restriction – along the lines of a low-calorie diet. Unlike a low-calorie diet that is time-limited, modified fasting can be open-ended. Meaning that you live your life eating a lower than usual amount of food on most days and then having a kind of day-off when you eat normally and even without any caloric restrictions. For example, the well-documented 5:2 diet is when you eat 500-600 calories a day for 5 days and you eat without any restrictions for 2 days, cycling through this kind of 5:2 schedule in an open-ended fashion as a baseline eating style.

Harm Reduction/Sublimation Sales Pitch

So what we have here is an obvious parallel between binge-eating and intermittent fasting. Some of these permutations of CR and IF, such as the 5:2 schedule closely approximate the dynamics of a binge-eating rollercoaster with its periodic over-controlled and under-controlled eating. Your harm reduction mission – if you dare accept it – is to inform your binge-eating client of this parallel. How? Simply by saying something along the following lines:

> *"Hey, I don't know if you are aware of this or not, but a lot of what you described actually parallels what is now known as intermittent fasting. Have you heard anything about that? It's a cutting edge approach to health maintenance. Let me tell you a little bit of what I know about it…"*

With this intro you proceed to educate the client briefly on intermittent fasting and the associated health and longevity benefits. Make sure that your client understands that you are not about to prescribe any kind of diet. You are simply pointing out a curious parallel and inviting the client to ponder it.

> *"Now that you've had a chance to learn about this a little I wonder what you are thinking… What comes to mind as you consider how what you've been trying to do intuitively for years parallels this promising health maintenance development…"*

Let your client think out loud a bit. Chances are that they will tell you that they are pleasantly surprised, that it all makes intuitive sense, that they are relieved to know that what they have been doing isn't all that bad, that they are wondering about where you are going with this. They might even ask: *"Are you saying that binge-eating is ok?"*

Explain that you don't really think about all of this in such terms:

"It is what it is for you. I am simply pointing out a curious parallel to you because I thought you'd be intrigued to know and I invite you to do some research of your own about this. Google® it and see what you find out."

The point here is to nudge an attitude shift. Remember that the name of the game here is attitudinal harm reduction, at least, as a starting point. We are not talking behavior change, we are talking a change in self-view. Leave the responsibility with the client: Bait them with this unexpected parallel and leave it up to them to explore it further. It's important not to oversell this. Plant the seed and let the client tend to it. That's about it. That's the clinical alchemy of sublimation.

A Progressive Referral

In the session to come, come back to this with a follow-up question along the following lines:

"Have you had a chance to look into this? What have you learned? And I wonder how all this new info is changing how you think about your eating style…"

Once again, our only harm reduction goal here is a change in narrative. Let the client set the pace for what follows. Let the client be the source of initiative. If the client seems excited and interested in cross-walking their free-form binge-eating lifestyle into some formalized IF paradigm, refer him or her to a progressive nutritionist or dietician who is familiar with CR and IF. And, of course, offer your own services to support this behavioral and attitudinal paradigm shift. Help the client see how mindful eating retraining in general and mindful emotional eating retraining – with its choice awareness and process mindfulness – can come in handy in making this behavioral shift. If, however, the client is not interested in formalizing their binge-eating into intermittent fasting (since to do so does require some behavioral fine-tuning), let this stay where it's at by allowing the client to keep this new, less self-stigmatizing perspective on their eating style.

And worry not; this isn't an impasse, just most likely a slow incubation period. Buy yourself some time by inviting the client to revisit the foundational goal of all mindful emotional eating retraining which is "leveraging more coping per calorie," which can be stated in a humanistically irresistible way as, "How about we talk about how you can get more enjoyment out of your eating style with the help of mindfulness?"

Chapter 10 | Hand to Mouth Trance: Calorically Sinless Vegging

No, we are not done with binge-eating yet. In this chapter we'll be talking about another harm reduction angle that you can attempt with your emotional eating client who joneses to numb out now and then. Some emotional eaters are only occasional binge-eaters and they value those moments. They just want to numb out. Maybe unlike the most devout binge-eaters, this particular type of client welcomes the general idea of down-shifting most binge-eating fantasies to emotional overeating, even mindful emotional eating. But, at the end of the day, they prefer to keep their options open. In these moments when they want to "just not be," eating is meant to work like a pacifier spiked with a horse tranquilizer. In these moments they are not interested in being, they are interested in non-being. They are not interested in mindfulness, they are interested in mindlessness. The target state is a hand-to-mouth trance, a state of no-mind, a reversible coma on demand.

Vegging

Vegging is perfect slang term for this kind of hand-to-mouth trance. All day long we have to be human and, what's more, humane. Not only are we expected to be on time, to be industrious, and so on and so forth, but we are also expected to be kind, compassionate, considerate and caring. That's a lot. No wonder we burn out. And the fauna that we are we fantasize about being flora. We yearn to just veg – to just be, like a blade of grass swaying in the breeze or to feel deeply rooted and grounded like an unpretentious sycamore in its drab green-gray camo jeans.

The thing to understand about vegging is that it's all body and no mind. And the body, frankly, doesn't care much about taste. Taste is the mind's business. Body doesn't want, it just needs. Mind wants, mind yearns, mind expresses preferences. Mind likes and dislikes. Body minds or doesn't mind. Give your body a carrot stick and it'll eat it. Give your mind a carrot stick and it'll scoff at it.

From Carrot Cakes Back to Carrots

Since vegging isn't about taste but about the hand-to-mouth trance, there is a harm reduction angle here to explore. The idea is simple: Mindfully choose what you will mindlessly binge on. Once again what is needed here is the clinical courage to work with what is. If your client likes to disappear into that binge-eating hand-to-mouth trance, help your client begin to see that ultimately it's not about what the client is eating but about mindless eating per se. Help the client understand and make conscious the soothing magic of this kind of mindless coping. Help the client see that after the first two or three potato chips, the taste becomes irrelevant and what matters is that there is still something left in the bag, what matters is that for a foreseeable future (of, say, a half hour or until "Wheel of Fortune" runs its course) there is a pacifier in the mouth. Help the client see that vegging is about giving yourself permission not to think, not to try, not to strive and that we accomplish this through a choice to regress, through a kind of adult version of sucking our thumbs.

Sucking our thumbs would look disturbing to our partners and kids so we cleverly shuttle something into our mouths – popcorn, candy, potato chips. In the final analysis, the foodstuff doesn't really matter; in a pinch, we'll eat a bag of frozen raviolis just to get by on something. So, all of this begs the conclusion: When it comes to vegging the taste is essentially irrelevant. And if so, why not shift from carrot cake to carrot sticks if what we really yearn for is just a thumb to suck on, simply the repetition of that all too familiar and regressively relaxing hand-to-mouth motion.

Harm Reduction Vegging

Harm reduction vegging is literally vegging. Invite your client to veg when he or she wants to veg. More specifically, explain the rationale. Explain that the taste doesn't matter beyond the first two or three mindless mouthfuls. And invite the client to think of vegging as the time to eat vegetables – mindlessly. Tell your client to save his or her mindfulness for something more appetizing. Merge the two connotations of the term "vegging" into one behavioral denotation: "When vegging, veg." Remind the client that veggies are an important part of human diet and that we often skimp out on them because they are not all that yummy. With this in mind, invite your client to use the desire to veg (to numb out, to eat mindlessly) for eating veggies. Give your client the permission to give himself or herself the permission not to pay attention to what he or she is eating as long as he or she is eating vegetables. Be explicit, like a rascal sage:

"If you want to eat and watch TV, you can. If you want to numb out and just eat something while you catch up on your DVR, you can. Mindfully choose what you will mindlessly eat while you watch TV. If you want to veg, then grab a handful of paper towels and slap a drainer full of fresh vegetables on your lap. And veg away. What a perfect time to load up on fiber and antioxidants. Think of it as taking meds or vitamins. We grab a handful, jerk our head back with a sip of water and we are done. No talk of mindfulness here. Same with veggies – if you want to veg, veg and save your mindful presence for later, for something more palatable and appetizing."

Mindfully Choose What You Will Mindlessly Eat

The scariest thing about harm reduction approach to emotional eating retraining is not the reaction of our clients but the reaction of our colleagues. The abstinence paradigm still has us in an all-or-nothing chokehold. The pressure to conform is immense. The specter of enabling still roams staff rooms and treatment team meetings. We are afraid to de-pathologize, to sublimate, to normalize. And our clients are hostages to our clinical fears. The permission to veg, particularly, when such a permission to eat mindlessly is issued mindfully, consciously and freely is not a moment of surrender but a moment of creative self-regulation and oral self-soothing, with the added benefits of fiber, vitamins and minerals. The idea is intuitive but we struggle to digest it. We choke up on dogma that "vegging" and "binging" is bad. The duality of all-or-nothing thinking as always falls on its own sword. Dare to try and experiment. After all, this curious field we are in is part science and part art, remember? Even if the experiment fails, even if vegging on veggies ends up becoming an all-out clean-out-your-pantry binge, your client has at least tried something new. And in that, there is a precedent of pattern interruption, a precedent of going off the autopilot, a precedent of conscious tweaking. And all that is how we eventually get unstuck.

Chapter 11 | Mindful Nighttime Eating

*I leave Sisyphus at the foot of the mountain. One
always finds one's burden again. But Sisyphus teaches the higher
fidelity that negates the gods and raises rocks. He too concludes that
all is well. This universe henceforth without a master seems to him
neither sterile nor futile. Each atom of that stone, each mineral
flake of that night-filled mountain, in itself, forms a world.
The struggle itself toward the heights is enough to fill
a man's heart. One must imagine Sisyphus happy.*

Albert Camus

• • • • • • •

The days of our lives seem to have Sisyphean circularity to them. One frustrating situation after another we push and push the boulder of cumulative stress up the day's hill only to be run over by it at the end of the day. It doesn't help that we keep piling on hard-to-fulfill expectations on ourselves: We promise to find a better way of coping, without eating, and we commit to start anew tomorrow morning. But tomorrow comes and this Sisyphean circle repeats itself; all day long we are trying to be good, taking care of business, managing frustration until the long-awaited evening comes and all we want to do is just sit back, watch a little TV and munch. Saying good night to an overwhelmed mind is no easy matter.

Five Types of Nighttime Emotional Eating

I distinguish five different kinds of nighttime eating: hermit eating, decompressing, reward eating, insomnia-related eating, sleep eating and metabolic nighttime eating. This, of course, is an informal taxonomy, just a way of sorting through the different nighttime eating scenarios. A better understanding of how your clients arrive at these emotional eating moments is essential for an effectively customized intervention. A nuanced perspective on the specific self-care fantasies that drive nighttime eating allow you, the clinician, to offer motive-specific, situation-specific validation. And that goes a long way.

Hermit Eating

Hermits want to be left alone. "Just being left alone" is a common self-care fantasy. Many of us are thrown into excessively public roles. All day long we are on some kind of display. We keep our mouths shut, we hide out behind our poker faces, we control and over-control our emotions to avoid any possible leak of intimacy. For whatever legitimate or perceived reason we feel we can't afford to just be ourselves. So, when the evening rolls around, we just want to be left alone, to be ourselves, not to have to perform for the audience (be it work-related or family-related). While we can't just curl up into a fetal pretzel (because even at home we can't always be alone), we can at least stick that proverbial thumb of self-soothing into our mouth and nurse ourselves a bit. And this is where hermit eating comes in. On some level we have long culturally understood that eating is a form of respite and with that comes the implicit understanding that you will be left alone. This mandate of privacy is for both ends of this metabolic business – for both excreting and eating. Most of the time, unless you have a toddler running around, people don't need to be reminded to leave you alone: They get it – you are eating or in the bathroom, it's personal time.

What I clinically see in this is an opportunity for a bit of assertiveness training. Hermit eating is a form of "me-time." And the run-away binge potential of hermit eating, at least, in part has to do with our hesitation to just ask to be left alone for a while. Instead of asking, we go for the "seconds" to buy us a few more minutes of being left alone while we eat. With this nuance in mind, help your client explore to what extent their nighttime eating has to do with their desire to be left alone. Keep in mind that not everyone has their own study, their own room or a finished basement to hide in. Many people hide out in kitchens. Ask your client point-blank: "Is this about eating or about being left alone?" And help the client explore what makes it difficult for them to assert their need for "me-time" more directly. What is needed here is some compassionate validation of the self-care motive, some choice awareness training and some assertiveness training.

Decompressing/Stress Eating

Nighttime decompressing is quintessential emotional eating. Eating, if you recall, signals the body to relax. Nighttime eating of this sort is a straightforward coping shortcut. It's too late to do yoga, too late for treadmill, too late to bother with meditation, too late to seek support because everyone is also fried or has gone to bed, so you park your butt in the kitchen and hit the parasympathetic reset button. I get it, sweet and simple. There is nothing to judge here just another mind trying to slow itself down a bit before bedtime. This kind of end-of-the-day decompressing is bonafide self-care. Validate it and offer to fine tune (more at the end of the chapter). What is needed here is compassionate validation of the self-care motive, some choice awareness training and stress management.

Reward Eating

Hang a carrot stick in front of a mule and it'll chase the unattainable all day long. We are our own slave drivers. We creatively incentivize ourselves to plough through the day in exchange for a yummy treat at the end of the day. We climb the day's cliffs and hold our breath like navy seals in times of frustration just to get to that treasured tête-à-tête with a pint of ice cream. And once we get to that long-awaited finish line of the day's marathon nothing can dissuade us from claiming our hard-earned prize. The problem is that we don't just stop there, we crash – not just because of the sugar high, but because of a moral low. We judge ourselves and, in so doing, we inadvertently set ourselves up for that "forget it." moment which, in turn, results in a nighttime binge. What is needed here is validation, self-acceptance and relapse prevention training.

Insomnia-related Eating

Many of your clients with nighttime eating are really insomniacs. They live their lives, have normal suppers without overeating, they wash up and go to bed. But then they toss and turn and get back up – to eat, banking on food as a kind of physiological lullaby. A wired mind takes a while to calm down and eating is a convenient parasympathetic shortcut. This pattern is easy to spot, your client will readily tell you that he or she was "not even hungry." What is needed here is validation of self-care, choice awareness training and some insomnia management.

Metabolic Nighttime Eating

Your body needs what it needs and it isn't shy about it. If it's hungry, it might just wake you up. This kind of nighttime eating is strictly metabolic in nature. If you are "being good" all day, skipping meals, calorie-restricting, or just plain too busy to eat, you just might have to do your eating at night. At the very least, your body might certainly show up on the door steps of your mind and awaken your drowsy self with a request for a midnight snack. What is needed here is better time management (if you skip meals because you don't have time for yourself) and possibly smarter eating that involves the so-called satiety extenders, particularly, as part of your evening meal. You see, foods vary in terms of how quickly they can be metabolized. Some foods break down fast and power us up in a jiffy. Other foods, with the so-called low glycemic index, take a while to break down. As a result, they provide a more sustainable release of energy and keep us full for longer. Incorporating such low glycemic foods into your evening meal may help you sleep through the night. See *Eating the Moment*, for details on how to leverage the so-called residual satiety (Somov, 2008).

The Art of Winding Down with Food

Whatever your particular Sisyphean boulder of daily angst is made of, here's a list of suggestions on how to keep it from flattening you on its way down:

- Give yourself a conscious permission to cope. Recognize that this nighttime eating episode is also an episode of self-care, not a relapse of self-destructiveness.

- Start your evening self-care routine with a course of relaxation: Take a few hum-ful breaths (to leverage the vaso-dilating, relaxing benefits of NO); consider such oronasal relaxation shortcuts as having a slow glass of warm milk or a glass of "calm-omile" to calm down.

- If proceeding to eat after this course of relaxation, wake yourself up: Draw a mindful circle, open your mind before you open your mouth.

- Proceed to eat mindfully, keeping your mind online with the help of pattern interruption techniques (e.g., eat with a non-dominant hand, use inconvenient utensils, change up the setting of your nighttime meal).

- When feeling emotionally relieved or fulfilled, or when you reach a point of moderate, pleasant fullness, get on the riverbank of metacognition – start pumping those self-control/craving-control brakes to prevent shifting into a binge-eating mode.

- Regardless of the caloric outcome of your nighttime eating, validate your coping motive and accept your coping effort: Your motives are pure, you were just trying to feel better (or not to feel at all), and you did your coping best (and that counts.).

These are pretty much generic mindful emotional eating suggestions – a baseline of sorts. Dress it up with scenario-specific twists.

- If your client yearns for time alone, offer them assertiveness training so that they don't have to rely on food to speak for them. Help them practice tactful yet direct ways of requesting to be left alone for a while to wind down.

- If your client forgets to eat and wakes up hungry in the middle of the night, a prudent first step would be time management and assertiveness training.

- If your client can't wait for that nighttime self-indulgence of ice cream, then a particular emphasis needs to be placed on cultivating the art of choice-aware, process-aware savoring with the help of pattern interruption and process mindfulness, and on relapse prevention training (to prevent a nighttime treat-eating from spiraling out of control).

- The client with a habit of nighttime decompressing would do well to get some extra relaxation training. The nighttime eater who eats because he or she can't fall asleep would naturally require insomnia management for DFA (difficulty falling asleep) as well as choice awareness training to remember to use behavioral insomnia management rather than rely solely on food to conk out. Which is not to say that the insomnia-related nighttime eater can't also benefit from a more mindful nighttime snack with an emphasis on mindfuls rather than mouthfuls. Furthermore, a bit of psycho-education and awareness-building on how overeating can keep us awake at night (through acid reflux, digestion stress and general somatic discomfort) would also help your insomnia-related nighttime eater.

The point here, as you see, is to take the basics of the mindful emotional eating and customize them to the specifics of a given nighttime eating scenario.

24/7 Self-Acceptance

Recognize that, by and large, nighttime eating is just a special case of your run-of-the-mill daytime emotional eating. Your client however is likely to bring it up as a stand-alone issue that is somehow separate from their general problems with emotional eating. For whatever reasons, in my experience, clients tend to think of nighttime emotional eating as a nutritional sin of the highest caliber. There tends to be more shame and more denial about it. With this in mind, you might have to work extra hard to de-pathologize nighttime eating. Err on the side of over-validation rather than under-validation. Don't be afraid to say, with emphasis:

> *"I get it. Your nighttime eating makes very good sense to me. You are fried, you are beat, you are drained. Evenings are tough. Nighttime is tough. The day has finally caught up with you and you just want what you want and you are done compromising. All you want to do is to just feel better or not feel at all. You just want to be left alone to have some time to yourself at the end of the day. You just want to have something nice, a treat of sorts, and go to sleep. I get it – it's self-care. There is no sin in any of this."*

Emotions don't stop at night. We suffer all day. Thus, mindful emotional eating is a 24/7 kind of affair. Whenever there is a desire for emotional eating, there is a good reason to make it mindful. Whenever there is a desire to cope by eating, there is an opportunity to leverage more coping per calorie with the help of mindful presence. Hesitate not to give your clients permission to cope by eating 24/7 so that they can eventually learn to be self-accepting around the clock. In my clinical opinion, it's this kind of 24/7 self-acceptance that is our best relapse prevention measure for mindless nighttime binge eating. The Sisyphean vicious cycle of stress and self-loathing about emotional eating can be helped. We just need to remember that life doesn't stop and coping is a full-time job. The daily grind renews itself each and every day, not waiting on us to catch up. Helping your client accept that they are doing their best with nightly coping is a great starting place for long-term change. And help your client not to worry about "being good." This daily business of "being good" tends to result in "being bad" at night. Dichotomous thinking always falls on its own sword. "Being mindfully nice" to yourself 24/7 is enough.

Yes, as a clinician, you are terrified of enabling. Worry not, by enabling self-acceptance you stand to enable self-control.

Chapter 12 | Building Mindful Eating Partnerships

Emotional eating is a lonely affair by definition. Ashamed and embarrassed, emotional eaters don't just hide from others, they also escape into mindlessness from themselves. The result is a life of eating secrecy. Emotional eaters are stealth eaters; if they eat in front of the refrigerator it's not because they are following Geneen Roth's suggestion of taking time for self-care but because they don't want to get busted red-handed, so they sneak-snack. This game of hide-and-seek naturally perpetuates the cycle of shame. This chapter is about coming out of the emotional eating closet.

Mindful Emotional Eating Partnership (MEEP)

A mindful emotional eating partnership (MEEP) is a relationship of support around emotional eating. MEEP is a relationship of understanding. Your MEE partner understands that emotional eating is inevitable and doesn't judge it. Your MEE partner understands that emotional eating is a legitimate coping strategy, that it is an attempt to feel better or not to feel bad, and that there is no sin in it. Your MEE partner understands that the problem isn't emotional eating per se but mindless emotional eating. Your MEE partner understands that the issue isn't emotional eating but emotional over-eating. Your MEE partner understands that mindful emotional eating is not a relapse but a relapse prevention measure, that it is designed to prevent emotional over-eating. Your MEE partner understands that mindful emotional eating is not about willpower, that it is a skill-set that involves choice awareness, process mindfulness and smart relaxation. In short, your MEE understands you, understands where you are coming from and, most importantly, understands where you are going with emotional eating.

Cultivating MEEPs

A partnership of this kind requires, at a minimum, three things: a shared knowledge base, an agreed-upon narrative of non-co-dependent support with clear boundaries and explicit understanding of reciprocation. Let me explain what I mean by these three variables.

Shared Knowledge Base

Your MEE partner must understand where you are coming from and where you are going with all this business of mindful emotional eating. They have to be just as well versed in the mindful emotional eating know-how as you are – at the very least, just as knowledgeable. They have to know why nasal breathing out is more effective than taking a deep breath. They have to have a pretty good idea of how to use pattern interruption as part of choice awareness. They have to have some experience of sitting on the riverbank of their metacognition so as to be able to remind you how to use it for craving control/impulse control purposes. They have to know the principles of mindful emotional eating so as to make sure that they don't inadvertently shoot you down with some abstinence-based judgment. In sum, they have to be willing to know how to support you in a pinch rather than wing it on nothing more than support and a serenity prayer.

Shared, Non-co-dependent Support Narrative

There is nothing like the hidden narcissism of codependence to get in the way of effective support. Your MEE partner must understand that they are not responsible for you or for your MEE outcomes. They should not fear enabling you because they understand that only you have the ultimate ability to do what you do. They should be willing to walk away from any kind of self-aggrandizing halo of being a rescuer or a savior or some other psychological VIP. They should be willing to simply understand, with tact and humility, that their role is that of a supportive coach assistant. No, not the coach, but coach assistant. They are not leading you to victory, they are simply reminding you of what you know about how to get to a desired mind-state. They don't feel burdened by your failures and they don't take credit for your success.

The Issue of Reciprocation

And furthermore they don't feel like you owe them something. They are clear that they are not being saintly but simply self-serving. Saints make us all look like sinners. A MEE partner neither makes you look good or bad. A

MEE partner is brutally sober about his or her motives. He or she is able to say: "Look, I am not doing this for you. I am doing this for me – you and I agreed to reciprocate and it is now my turn. You owe me nothing. It's a tit-for-tat. So, relax. Stop apologizing and let's talk about your objectives for this mindful emotional eating episode." In setting up a MEEP it is essential to find someone who struggles with similar issues so that any given instance of MEE support is mutually beneficial. This way both parties learn from the experience. With this in mind, I initially discourage recruiting MEEPs from spouses and partners. Often times, our stress is related to our significant relationships. While a mindful emotional eating episode is an emotionally intimate connection, you don't want to get bogged down in the discussion of why you are upset with your partner since he or she is hardly an objective party to deal with that. What is needed is a neutral enough party – a friend, better yet an acquaintance.

Basic Steps

The basic steps to cultivate mindful emotional eating support are as follows:

1. Identify a potential MEE partner.
2. Discuss with him/her the idea behind mindful emotional eating, get on the same page.
3. Do a few hypothetical dress-rehearsals on what is expected and how a MEEP would work.
4. Explicitly address the issue of personal responsibility to prevent any concerns about enabling and/or caregiver guilt.
5. Discuss frequency/rules of engagement/any applicable boundaries.
6. Agree to pilot this mindful emotional partnership for no longer than three months and plan to formally re-assess how it's working.
7. Re-assess the success of the partnership, exchange feedback, modify, if necessary, the rules of engagement and/or gracefully dissolve the partnership.

Making Use of MEEPs

When feeling emotionally upset and considering mindful emotional eating as a coping intervention, get your MEEP on the phone and let them know what you are trying to do. Tell them that you are upset or stressed and that you decided to cope by eating mindfully. Show them your cards, explain that while you are not exactly hungry, you'd like to supplement comfort food with the comfort of supportive company. Ask if your MEEP is willing to just be with you, without judgment, as you take your time to mindfully snack a bit. Explain that you are not looking for therapy or advice, just for someone to be with you, to help you stay mindful while you cope by eating. Clarify that you are not looking for them to solve your problems.

While a few years ago I would suggest to my clients that they should try to "process" what upsets them with their MEEPs, my mind has changed on the matter: a better use of the mindful emotional eating partnership is for maintaining mindfulness and *not* for a discussion of what stressed and upset you. This kind of emotional analysis is too free form and it gets in the way of the actual mindful emotional eating. A discussion of what happened and how you feel about it and why you need to cope with it by eating becomes too chaotic and the point of practicing mindful emotional eating is lost. Instead, my current recommendation is to simply ask your MEE partner to help you stay mindful during this coping episode.

If you find yourself on the other side of this intervention, as a MEE partner, do your best to avoid being judgmental of emotional eating. Your job is to remind the other person of the fact that they have a particular method of coping, that they know what to do and you are there on a kind of standby to help them stay on track. That's it. Ask them and/or tell them:

What is your coping intention?

Have you had a chance to wake yourself up with a bit of pattern interruption?

Now would be a good time to go ahead and wake yourself up: Draw a mindful circle.

Have you had relaxation as your first course?

Now would be a good time to have some relaxation as your first course.

Tell me what you decided to eat mindfully.

What pattern interruption techniques will you use to keep yourself present during eating?

Would eating with a non-dominant hand help?

Would eating while standing help?

Would it help if you used chopsticks with your bowl of cereal to keep your mind present?

Now take your time to have a few mindfuls.

Pause for a second and let's talk about what it's like in this moment?

Are you now feeling better? Are you feeling the way you wanted?

You mentioned getting seconds. Now might be a good time to sit on the riverbank a bit and watch the cravings come and go as you focus on your breath.

If you feel that the emotional eating episode is gradually becoming an episode of emotional overeating, remind yourself that you are not responsible for the other's eating behavior and make your concern known in the form of feedback:

I am not there so I am not sure what is going on but I am beginning to wonder if this episode of emotional eating is becoming an episode of emotional overeating. How do you yourself feel about how this is playing out? Let's talk about what your current coping intention is.

With this contingency in mind, it helps to ask from the beginning:

Hey, I'd love to be there with you as you take care of yourself...
Do you want me to encourage you to slow down a bit and remind you to not overdo?

If yes, then do. If no, then just be there for them, with them, without judgment. This kind of role induction can help both of you avoid any awkwardness. Also, as part of role induction it might be useful to set a time limit for a mindful emotional eating episode. As a MEE partner you can say from the outset:

I have about five minutes. Let's get started, ok?

And when you feel that this coping episode is beginning to take more time than you can currently afford simply excuse yourself and say:

Hey, I hope this helped. I am sorry but I do have to go. You seem to be off to a good start. You seem to know what to do. So, it's all you from here. Let me know how it worked out. But I do want to give you kudos for reaching out and approaching emotional eating in this kind of mindful manner. Congrats on mindful coping.

As you see, it helps to be direct and to the point. This kind of matter-of-fact attitude takes the crisis out of this emotional eating episode. Your work-like tone conveys calmness. It normalizes what is going on. There is no crisis here, just another attempt at conscious, mindful coping.

At the end of this coping episode, your last task as MEE partner is to help your opponent acknowledge the success of this coping endeavor. The very fact that they reached out to you is already an important precedent. The very fact that they set out to cope by eating mindfully, with intention and a plan is a clear mark of progress. The very fact that they made the first steps (of waking their mind through pattern interruption and then calming their mind through relaxation) is a big deal and should be acknowledged as such. In other words, be prepared to help the coping person see that their motive was psychologically healthy and that their effort reflects their moment-specific best. Try to conclude on a supportive note:

You did your best. Let's make sure we acknowledge that.
Good going! Glad for you!

It might also be useful to remind your opponent that they owe you nothing, that you too benefited from this moment:

Listen, I learned a lot from this moment too. It helps me to see how this works since I myself, as you know, struggle with this issue. Helping you with this mindful emotional eating episode is a good dress rehearsal for me as well. So, thanks for reaching out and giving me a chance to be mindful of this coping option that I too have.

End on the same matter-of-fact note as you begin. This doesn't have to be a super-sappy bonding moment. While it is special and laden with emotional intimacy, it is also, in a way, nothing special – just another learning opportunity, just another precedent of conscious coping. Making a super-big deal about this is unnecessary drama. Treat this as a routine encounter in a two-way mindful emotional eating partnership. Nothing more, nothing less.

Your First MEEP

It goes without saying that developing these kinds of mindful emotional eating partnerships will take time. With this in mind, it helps to not wait and to get started right away. Finding a local therapist to work with you in this manner might be a great way to get started quickly. Or, if you are already in therapy, see if your current therapist would be willing to work with you in this manner. Explain that you are not necessarily looking for on-call support but merely for a chance to process your emotional eating episodes in session. Introduce your therapist to this idea, explain how it works and what you are trying to do and see if they would be willing to coach you on this. And, of course, if your therapist is willing to offer you this kind of support in real time by phone then that would be really great. There might or might not be a financial stipulation that comes with this. Which brings up a point for you to consider: How valuable is this kind of real time support to you? If you feel it would be worth it to you to pay for it, then let your therapist know and perhaps the two of you can arrive at a coaching arrangement that is mutually beneficial. After all, most therapists don't like on-call work. Alternatively, check to see if your therapist would be able to bill your insurance for this kind of after-hours, on-demand assistance.

If all falls through and you don't know anyone who can enter into a reciprocal MEE partnership with you, check to see if you can hire a life coach. Explain that you are looking for a set of frontal lobes for hire, so to say. Explain that you are working on a specific awareness-building/habit-modifying project and that you need someone to help you stay on track. Have them familiarize themselves with this book, with this chapter, in particular, and take it from there. Or, if you can't afford life coaching, see if you can mobilize your social media resources to start your own network of MEE support. Dare to offer MEE-style support and you will likely get it in return. Finally, feel free to call out for MEE-type support on Mindful Eating Tracker, a feature on my book site (www.eatingthemoment.com) where my readers come to share their mindful eating moments and support each other in their mindful eating endeavors.

—⚘—

Chapter 13 | Mindful Emotional Eating and Weight Management

If you eat normally most of the time and do not binge,
you will be able to maintain a stable weight even if you occasionally eat
for emotional reasons. However, if you want to lose weight, you may
need to work harder to reduce the frequency of emotional eating.
Linda Craighead, *Appetite Awareness Workbook*

• • • • • • •

Emotional eating has been a long-standing bugaboo in the diet literature. Many wars have been waged on emotional eating and just as many have been lost. Emotional eating has been the villain of weight loss, the ominous relapse factor that heralds that short-lived moment of "forget it," self-liberation from self-imposed dietary constraints. This kind of history comes with momentum – the prejudice against emotional eating is not to be underestimated. With this in mind, as a clinician who is willing to offer mindful emotional eating retraining, you'd do well to be prepared for addressing the following question: "How does mindful emotional eating play into weight management?" This chapter is the answer to this question.

MEE Assures the Longevity of a Dieting Effort

If your client is on a diet, it's their business. If they ask you about what you think about diets, you can tell them and then it's their business again as to how they are going to integrate your opinion about dieting. My opinion is that diets sell books but don't really work. Diets are based on self-denial and self-denial is exhausting. Self-denial is a lousy platform for long-term self-change. Self-denials run us down. Diets are made of endless "No's" to yourself and that depletes our egos, impoverishes our quality of life, and weakens our capacity for self-control. A good bit of emotional eating is compensatory in nature, a reaction to diet-based self-deprivation. Let's face it – diets are stressful. With all of this in mind, we can conclude that mindful emotional eating not as a threat to a diet (if you have to be on one) but is a kind of maintenance mechanism. It's pretty much inevitable – whether you are on a diet or not – that sooner or later you'll feel like you want to take a coping shortcut by eating. Whenever you develop this urge, if you are lacking ego resources to white-knuckle your way through it, you'll be faced with a decision point: To eat to cope or not to eat to cope. A cookie has never killed anyone. I'd rather you mindfully indulge in a cookie or two than keep white-knuckling your way through this craving until you exhaust yourself, totally break down and binge. Seen this way, mindful emotional eating is an ally to dieting, not an enemy; a stabilizing, relapse prevention measure rather than a catastrophic regimen threat. In sum, my thesis is this: Mindful emotional eating assures the longevity of your dieting effort.

MEE Is Itself a Weight Loss Factor

Whether you are on a diet or not, emotional eating, as a temptation, is always around the corner. Mindless emotional eating, despite its modest beginnings, often insidiously grows into a binge. What starts out as a small indulgence not infrequently becomes an abstinence violation effect "forget it." moment. Indeed, you decide: "I'll just have a serving of ice cream… I've been good all week, I deserve it." Of course, you do. Who doesn't deserve ice cream? The problem is that a) you are not hungry, and b) you've got a TV remote in your hand. So, as you plug into the mindless matrix of TV, your mind goes AWOL and before you know it your body is full but your mind is still empty – empty of pleasure and satisfaction, that is, as you feel that you didn't even notice the ice cream. So, you head for seconds because you didn't have the firsts in the first place. But then the story repeats: your body has the seconds, but your mind – plugged into TV – remains devoid of conscious experience. So, you head out for the thirds and somewhere around that time you decide: "forget it. It's a binge, I'll get back on track tomorrow."

The point is that mindless emotional eating almost always results in overeating. Mindful emotional eating is different, its very point is conscious pleasure, savoring, being in the moment, noticing the experience and benefiting from it. As such, mindful emotional eating is fundamentally more satisfying. As mentioned before, mindful emotional eating leverages more coping per calorie. As a result, you have a moment of nutritionally unnecessary but emotionally necessitated pleasure and you don't overeat all that much. Sure, you still eat more than you would have had you just been eating to satisfy hunger. But the point is that you don't stuff yourself. Put differently, mindful emotional eating is self-limiting. Mindful, effective emotional eating stops itself. So, when you contrast the two – mindless emotional eating and mindful emotional eating – the latter is less nutritionally hazardous. With all things taken into consideration, if you are able to make a shift from mindless emotional eating to mindful emotional eating, you will end up eating less. And as such, with all other lifestyle factors being equal, mindful emotional eating can be seen as a weight loss factor in and of itself.

MEE Is a Relapse Prevention Factor

A slip is when you want to eat to cope and you don't. You waiver but you regain your composure – through willpower or skillpower, by white-knuckling or through impulse control and relaxation. A lapse is when you go ahead and have an emotional eating episode. A relapse is when, having lapsed once, you say "forget it." to yourself and go off track. Catching yourself, not at the moment of the slip, but in the process of the lapse and deciding that instead of having a mindless emotional eating episode (that is likely to become a binge and derail you for days) you will have a mindful emotional eating episode is a quintessential relapse prevention measure. It's harm reduction: Instead of mindlessly having a bag of cookies, you mindfully and consciously choose to have two or three; as a result, instead of having a lapse of control, you have a sense of regained control. And in so doing, you prevent an open-ended relapse. The train off the track, dangerously lurches as if about to fall into the abyss of dysregulation, but does, nevertheless, touch all of its wheels on the other end of this precarious business of controlled eating. A happy end.

MEE Is an Asset Not a Liability

In sum, mindful emotional eating is an asset not a liability – an ally not an enemy to any weight management project. Sure, it's counterintuitive but so is parallel parking. Worry not, you'll figure it out. As a clinical adviser, once again have the courage to encourage your client to experiment. Fear not the consequence: Mindful eating, like anything of value, has a reasonably steep learning curve. So, it's important to see where you are going with all of this lest you lose sight of the destination. Help your client see the rationale behind mindful emotional eating. Explain as much as you can and leave it to the client to choose to try or not to try, to dare or not to dare, to change or not to change. The ultimate responsibility for the outcome is on your client, not on you. Stay modest in your clinical mandate as an advisor and a consultant, and that'll help you not fear the consequence of your client's trials and errors. But should you allow your own fears get in the way, your client will be stuck in a stifling and disempowering mindset of abstinence and self-mistrust.

Chapter 14 | Mindless Emotional Eating Prevention

My previous work as a clinical director of a drug and alcohol treatment program in a county jail convinced me that the path of recovery, to a large extent, hinges on how we define what constitutes a relapse. That clinical experience, perhaps more so than any other, taught me about the importance of a humanistic approach to relapse prevention training. And this is what this chapter is about. The task in front of us is to delineate a relapse prevention program that, indeed, prevents a relapse rather than facilitates it. Towards this end, our relapse prevention ideology has to reflect the harm reduction psychology that underlies my approach to managing emotional eating.

Prevention and Harm Reduction

In a moment we will delve into arguably pretty dry clinical stuff – we'll talk about progressively finite distinctions between *slip*, *lapse* and *relapse* in the context of emotional eating. We'll go even deeper into different ways of defining these three depending on whether you are coming from an abstinence mindset or harm reduction mindset. To prevent losing your attention, reader, let me point out one very important point which is this: Harm reduction is a reduction of an extreme way of thinking. The abstinence model consists of two extremes: abstinence (being good) and relapse (being bad). Harm reduction takes this merciless black-and-white dichotomy and populates it with an infinite continuum of colorful distinctions. Harm reduction re-infuses the nuance of life back into this artificially sterilized set of all-or-nothing polarities. Harm reduction – by creating ever finer definitions of partial success – creates an endless series of self-forgiving U-turns. And in this is all the compassion and all the clinical wisdom of acceptance. So, what might strike you as pretty dry clinical stuff is really the very stuff that lubricates the process of humanistic change.

Slip, Lapse, and Relapse

Emotional eating, as previously posited, is inevitable. With this in mind, an abstinence-focused relapse prevention program would be utterly counterproductive. We would have to altogether ban emotional eating and any emotional eating episode would constitute a bonafide relapse. To my clinical mind, it's a non-starter. We have absolutely no clinical interest in banning this powerful coping option. Our clinical goal is not to eliminate emotional eating but to make it more effective and smarter by making it more mindful. The goal has been and is not abstinence but harm reduction – i.e. to help your client shift from mindless emotional eating to mindful emotional eating.

So, whereas from the abstinence stand-point any emotional eating is a problem to prevent, from the stand point of humanistic harm reduction, only *mindless* emotional eating is a problem to prevent. This, of course, entirely recalibrates the meaning of slip, lapse and relapse in this context.

Slip

If your goal or your client's goal is to altogether abstain from emotional eating, then any desire to cope by eating constitutes a slip. A slip, as the word implies, is when you literally lose balance as would be the case when you are walking down the street and you slip up on a banana peel. So, once again, if your goal is to never eat to cope again, to avoid any and all emotional eating – as unrealistic as it sounds – then any craving to veg, to binge, or to just eat for pleasure would be considered a slip, a loss of balance, a beginning of a fall (a beginning of a lapse). But abstinence from emotional eating is not our goal. Our goal is not to cut out emotional eating altogether but to make it more mindful. Therefore, the meaning of slip acquires a very different meaning. We will henceforth define a slip here as a desire to engage in an episode of mindless emotional eating.

Say you have read this book – as a clinician or a client – and now you know that emotional eating is not a sin but just a form of coping and that it can be fine-tuned and made more mindful. But, as the inertia of habit would have it, you don't feel like messing with it. So, next time you feel like having something to munch on when you are stressed, you decide that you just want to "take it easy," that you'll just do what you usually do and you'll mess with all this business of mindful emotional eating some other time. This desire to not trouble yourself with change isn't a sin, there is nothing catastrophic about any of this. You are simply defaulting to your habitual way of taking care of yourself.

This voice in your head that says "maybe later" and "I don't want to be mindful about this right now" is just the voice of habit, the voice of history. We'll talk about what to do about this in the next section. But at this point allow yourself to simply redefine the meaning of slip in this context. To clarify, it's not the desire to eat to cope that is problematic here but a desire to do so mindlessly, without awareness, without conscious presence. Once again, this isn't really any kind of big deal – this isn't the end of life or some kind of moral crisis. You are just craving a simple release, something familiar and comfortable. I get it and I hope you get it too: You have the rest of your life to work on this and whether you are eating to cope mindlessly or mindfully right now probably doesn't make that much of a difference.

Lapse

From the standpoint of the abstinence paradigm, a lapse would be a single episode return to emotional eating. So, if your goal is to never engage in another emotional eating episode (which sounds radical and unrealistic) than any one-time re-engagement in emotional eating would constitute a lapse. The word lapse literally means a fall. So, whereas a slip is a loss of balance, a lapse is an actual fall. So, from the standpoint of abstinence, having a desire to eat to cope is a slip and acting upon this desire once is a lapse.

A harm reduction view here is quite different. In fact, there are two ways for us to define a lapse here. Recall that we just defined a slip as a desire to eat to cope mindlessly (rather than mindfully). Acting upon this desire and actually engaging in an episode of mindless emotional eating would then constitute a lapse.

Alternatively, we can also look at a lapse here as a lapse of awareness. Say you or your client decided to try out a mindful emotional eating episode but somewhere along the lines what began as a mindful emotional eating episode ends up becoming a mindless emotional eating binge. That would be a lapse… a collapse of mindfulness… a falling asleep.

Is that a big deal? Should we lose our sleep over it? Should we beat ourselves up because of this? Not at all. A lapse of either kind is entirely probable and normal. You and your client are fighting a long-standing habit. There will be speed bumps. The circularity of the past will now and then reassert itself. These slips and lapses are part of the learning curve. Recall that mindful emotional eating is not a test of willpower but a project of cultivating skillpower. And that takes practice with its inevitable process of trial and error.

Relapse

Once again, in defining a relapse it is useful to juxtapose our definition of relapse with the definition of a relapse from the abstinence standpoint. So, if your goal is to never eat for emotional reasons – as self-denying and unrealistic as that might be – then a relapse is when, having lapsed, you lapse again and again and again. That's the "re-" part of re-lapse. To relapse literally is to fall again, with "re-" being a prefix of repetition. An abstinence-based view of relapse in terms of emotional eating would be a situation where having violated your self-denying and unrealistic oath-to-self to never eat to cope, you do end up lapsing – i.e. eating to cope – and then you decide "forget it." and you stop trying not to eat to cope altogether and you return to eating to cope all the time. This complete, dramatic, radical return to not trying at all anymore is rooted in the all-or-nothing mentality of the abstinence paradigm. What starts out as a "never again" falls hard on its own dichotomous sword of all-or-nothing thinking.

From the standpoint of humanistic harm reduction, a relapse can be defined in a couple of different ways. First, we can look at relapse as a re-loss of mindfulness. Say you sit down to try out a mindful emotional eating episode. But after a few mindfuls you tune out, your awareness flags and you are back to eating mindlessly. That's a lapse. So, you wake yourself back up with switching up your hands or some other pattern interruption trick. But after a while your mindfulness flags again – that would be a re-loss of consciousness, yet another re-occurrence of falling asleep while eating.

Another way to define a relapse is on a macro-level as a return to mindless emotional eating after the initial lapse into mindless emotional eating. So, say you start your program of shifting to mindful emotional eating on Monday. But by Wednesday you lapse – you ended up eating for emotional reasons mindlessly. And following this lapse, on Thursday you decided to not worry about mindful emotional eating until your next therapy session or until your MEE partner is back from vacation. That would be a relapse.

Is relapse into mindless emotional eating that big of a deal? It can be if we choose to look at it that way. But we can also choose to look at a relapse as yet another speed bump on the road to mindful emotional eating, as yet another learning opportunity, as a chance to fine tune your relapse prevention program which is what we discuss next.

SP, LP, RP

SP is slip prevention. LP is lapse prevention. RP is relapse prevention. Each act of prevention here is slightly different. So, let's take a closer look at what's involved.

SP= Slip Prevention

Slip, as we defined it, is a desire to not bother with mindful emotional eating. Therefore slip prevention is an attempt to prevent mindless emotional eating and to encourage mindful emotional eating instead. You have three prevention options here: motivational review, relaxation and riverbank attitude. Motivational review is a quick attempt to remind yourself of why you are trying to shift from mindless emotional eating to mindful emotional eating. It's a cheerleading kind of moment. Relaxation is a chance for you to cool off a bit before you rush to cope. Maybe once you feel a little better after the first course of relaxation, the urgency to mindlessly rush into emotional eating would pass and you would feel more up to trying out a more mindful approach to emotional eating. Riverbank attitude can also help; notice the urge to go back to mindless eating and let it pass. Maybe what shows up next in your mind is an impulse to try out mindful emotional eating. If so, get off the metacognitive riverbank and act upon that impulse. Given all these options, start with relaxation – just to nix that urgency to mindlessly rush into eating. And then spend a minute or two on that riverbank. Starting off with the motivational review hardly makes sense: When you are stressed, you will argue in favor of the path of least resistance. So, relax first, then step back in your mind and only then remind yourself of why you are interested in learning how to use emotional eating in a more effective, mindful manner.

LP= Lapse Prevention

We have defined lapse as a loss of consciousness during the actual mindful emotional eating episode. And we have also defined lapse as a one-time, stand-alone occurrence of mindless emotional eating. Two points here. If we look at a lapse here as a one-time occurrence of mindless emotional eating then slip prevention is de facto lapse prevention. If, however, we look at a lapse as a loss of presence in the course of what was supposed to be a mindful emotional eating episode, then lapse prevention is really about keeping your mind awake. And this is where choice awareness, pattern interruption and stimulus control come in. To keep your mind from falling asleep, keep it guessing, keep breaking patterns, use such pattern breaks as eating with wrong utensils or using a non-dominant hand. That sort of thing.

If it helps, change the setting where you eat. By using a designated location for mindful emotional eating you stand to condition yourself to be more awake and more alert when you eat to cope. This new setting can be a room that you usually doesn't eat in, or a chair that you don't usually eat in, or say a specific step on a flight of stairs in your home – any arbitrary location can serve as a kind of beeping alarm clock for your mind. The message here is: "This is where I eat to cope mindfully." To prevent a lapse of mindfulness, to keep your mind from falling asleep, it also helps to turn the TV off and not to eat in front of your computer or be on your smart phone. All of these electronic entertainment devices compete for consciousness and you only have so much of it to deploy on mindful emotional eating. "To stay awake, stay away from what puts your mind to sleep" is how I sometimes sum up this stimulus control lapse prevention strategy to my clients.

RP= *Relapse Prevention*

We defined relapse as a semi-permanent return to mindless emotional eating or as a continuous struggle to stay mindful in the course of a mindful emotional eating episode. The latter – the re-loss of mindful presence – should be tackled the same way as any lapse of consciousness during an emotional eating episode, that is, with the help of choice awareness, pattern interruption and stimulus control. As for giving up on mindful emotional eating because you have lapsed once, this is where decatastrophizing comes in. As you have probably noticed above, I've tried to model this attitude of decatastrophizing by reminding you, the reader, that neither a slip nor a lapse nor a relapse itself is a catastrophe of any kind. Each and every time I have rhetorically asked "Is this a big deal?" and answered my own question in the negative, I was trying to model an attitude of humanistic acceptance.

> *"Mindful emotional eating takes time to learn. There will be a learning curve. Defaulting to the old habits isn't a sin but a pursuit of wellbeing on the historical autopilot. All of this is normal. Grist for the learning mill. Part of a change process. What drives you is self-care. And you are doing your moment-specific best. That's enough for me and I hope that's enough for you."*

As a clinician, these ideas have become second nature to me. I de-catastrophize without thinking about it. When I rattle off these phrases, I know I sound like a broken record and I also know that I am helping my clients mend their perception of their success record. Your best strategy here, clinician, is to offer an overkill of acceptance, to stand your ground of compassion until your client begins to internalize this attitude. Sooner or later your client will see how this way of thinking helps them reset and move on and let go of what was and to focus on what is and what is next. And that is the essence of relapse prevention – to keep the process of change flowing on and on, by breaking through the dam of self-criticism and self-deprecation.

Develop a Shared Prevention Narrative

Let's face it: All this prevention business is pretty dry clinical stuff. It's boring to read about but it's anything but boring when it comes to application. Slip-lapse-relapse prevention is essential for long-term success. It is paramount that you do not overlook it. And it's not just enough to understand it yourself, clinician – it's just as important to help your client start thinking about how he or she will recover from these speed bumps on the road of change. It's essential that the two of you explicitly develop a shared prevention narrative. Agree on the terms in advance. Talk about how the two of you will make sense of the trial-and-error nature of the change process. Prime your client's mind for a methodical, decatastrophizing change stance. Help them not fear mistakes. Help your client see way beyond the slip, beyond the lapse, and, most importantly, beyond the relapse. Help your client see all the way to success.

Chapter 15 | Eastern Fullness, Eastern Emptiness

The Dao is present in emptiness.
Emptiness is the fasting of the mind.
Zhuangzi

• • • • • • •

The esoteric magic of the East, I posit, begins with a very different view of food than the one that we, the modern-day Westerners, have. As far as I can tell this rather sobering view of food and eating goes way, way back.

Vedic Insight: Trinity of Eating

Taittireya Upanishad, one of the ancient Indian sacred texts written in Sanskrit almost 3000 years ago, proclaims:

> *"I am food, I am food, I am food. I am the eater of food, I am the eater of food, I am the eater of food. I am the uniter, I am the uniter, I am the uniter."*

A theosophical analysis of this may suggest something as nuanced as the idea that you are both the object and the subject of the experience, and that, at the same time, you are neither. A religious analysis would ratchet this up to something along the Vedic lines of: "I am the manifest and the unmanifest, the Brahman and the Atman, form and essence." The exact implicit meaning of this ancient idea is well beyond the scope of this book. But the explicit meaning of it is pretty straightforward: Made of Earth, we are Earth itself, Earth that is eating itself with each and every mouthful. At the surface level there is the basic notion of metabolic transmutation: We are what we eat and in due time we too become food, with the act of eating itself being tantamount to living.

And it's in this secular interpretation of this ancient poetic line that I see the birth of mindful eating. You see, mindful eating is not unemotional eating. On the contrary, mindful eating is hyper-emotional eating. But, unlike our traditional emotional eating which is really about coping with suffering, mindful eating is the kind of emotional eating that celebrates the here-and-now of this existence. The emotionality of mindful eating is of the positive kind; mindful eating is eating with passion, with gusto, with heightened awareness. Thus, mindful eating, which is historically rooted in ancient poetizing of self-transcendence, is a moment of eating triumph in which we cognize ourselves in all of our trivial trinity: as eaters now, as food one day, and as the very act of eating.

Ancient mystics that learned to celebrate food were painfully and ecstatically aware of their own impermanence and saw moments of eating as an opportunity to anchor ourselves, if only for a moment, in an act of eating or non-eating.

Ahimsa: Empathic Eating

Ahimsa is a Sanskrit term for "non-violence." The ethics of non-violence were developed by Jains, an ancient school of thought from India. The philosophical and spiritual core of this ancient Vedic doctrine is a kind of pre-Christian "thou shall not kill" commandment as applied to *all* living beings. It should be clarified that ahimsa is not a do-no-harm philosophy – some harm is inevitable. Ahimsa doctrine is a harm-reduction philosophy that aims to minimize one's karmic footprint to a minimum. In Jain tradition, this doctrine took the form of vegetarianism and veganism. Ahimsa-eating is thus a form of ethical eating. It's a way of eating that is profoundly democratic, a way of eating that doesn't monopolize the circle of life and serves to keep human ego in check.

As such, ahimsa-style eating is conscious eating, eating with grace and gratitude to life-forms that fuel our minds and bodies. Thus, ahimsa-style eating (veganism, vegetarianism) has had a built-in element of mindfulness about it from the get-go. And this mindfulness was of the empathic kind, and therefore emotional. The point is this: Any mindful eating that is based in the ethics of non-violence is at its core a form of emotional eating, with compassion as its emotional vector.

This realization is essential in the context of this book and this program. By helping your client shift from mindless emotional eating to mindful emotional eating, we are not throwing the baby of emotionality out with the bathwater of mindless coping. What we are doing is actually changing the vector of emotionality – from palliative and coping in nature to empathic and celebratory. Mindful eating, particularly the kind that is motivated by the ethics of compassion, is inevitably emotional at its foundation. Yet the crux of its emotionality is not self-focused but other-focused. And that is the paradoxical shift that your client stands to make – instead of trying to reduce negative, self-centered emotionality through mindless eating your client stands to learn how to dial up positive, other-centered emotionality of compassion and gratitude via mindful, conscious eating. In my professional and personal experience, mindful eating eventually leads to ahimsa-style eating. An awakened mind usually comes with a bleeding heart which is both a blessing and a curse.

Santhara: Full Life on an Empty Stomach

Santhara is an ancient Jain tradition of a death by fasting and it is rooted in the doctrine of ahimsa (non-violence). The vow of santhara is not a suicide. Suicide, in its psychology, is a form of avoidance, an escape from pain, shame, embarrassment, or consequence. Santhara is anything but an impulse to run from what is. It is a profound decision to stay with what is. Unlike a suicide which may be triggered by a loss of meaning, santhara is arguably the most meaningful phase in Jain's spiritual life. The rationale is simple: karmic detox. To Jains, eating is the necessary evil, a zero-sum calamity of living. Jains have long understood that to eat we have to kill – to kill something or at least to rob some other life form of its own metabolic resources. Jains, the originators of the doctrine of ahimsa (non-violence), devote their life to minimizing harm to other sentient beings, and voluntary cessation of eating is the last, one-way attempt at manifesting this spiritual value. On average, a couple hundred or so Jains each year take this very slow way out of existence. I can't think of a slower way out of this life than through a one-way fast. But these folks know what they are doing, they know how to take their time, they know how not to run, they know how to be. Santhara is a hard-earned spiritual privilege; young folks with family obligations are not allowed this one-way spiritual experiment.

Santhara is not a response to existential emptiness but a manifestation of one's sense of existential fullness. Santhara is allowed when one has no more earthly desires, in other words, when one is full and content with life. Santhara is voluntary but it is under community regulation – the decision is publicly announced and the permission from one's family and/or community is requested. There is nothing rash or impulsive about this; criteria have to be met and proper motivations have to be evident. Santhara is not about giving up control – on the contrary it is one last powerful act of self-determination.

So, what are we to glean from this radical path to enlightenment? Certainly, I am not advocating this (it wouldn't be my spiritual place to do so). My purpose here is to simply introduce you to the possibility that a full life can be lived on an empty stomach. Nothing more, nothing less.

Oryoki: Process Focus

Oryoki is Japanese for "just enough." An Oryoki meal is an eating meditation associated with certain schools of Buddhism. It is a highly choreographed, highly methodical approach to eating that follows a strict procession of cues to keep the mind focused on the process of eating. On the technical side, an *oryoki* meal comes with its own gear. It includes a set of nested wooden bowls (*jihatsu*), the largest of which (*zuhatsu*) is called the Buddha bowl. *Oryoki* has an element of Buddhist liturgy as it is punctuated with built-in pauses for chanting prayer and expressing grace or gratitude. The meal ends with an opportunity for the donation of leftovers. Oryoki is well alive in Zen monasteries. And you can get an introduction to this eating ritual in some Buddhist retreat centers around the world.

The rationale behind the evolution of this eating ritual is complex and I suspect that in addition to the obvious spiritual benefits of conscious awareness there might have also been an administrative motive. Indeed, imagine that you are in charge of running (managing) a Buddhist monastery. You get all kinds of dharma bums seeking refuge…and free room and board. So, you come up with a bright idea – you turn the dining hall into a meditation hall. This way you make sure that all these monks actually mean business. After all, a hungry stomach comes with an attentive mind. Whoever controls the food sets the agenda. And if the agenda is mindful living then what better way to practice that than through mindful eating? Furthermore, Oryoki-style mindful eating has the added benefit of conserving the resources – also a point of administrative significance.

The tradition of Oryoki and other similar Eastern traditions of mindful food consumption (such as a tea ceremony) are a form of process mindfulness. The emphasis is on de-automatization and paying attention. "When you eat, just eat" is the party line that drives this way of being. This is, of course, quite similar to our own use of choice awareness, pattern interruption, process mindfulness, and meta-cognitive impulse control which doubles up as a concentration practice. Somewhat in contrast to what I have been asserting above about mindful eating being a form of emotional eating, Oryoki-style eating, in its highly structured form, actually strikes me as a way of assuring that eating is just eating. Oryoki-style eating is a concentration practice that flushes out the emotionality of eating. While an Oryoki practitioner might pause to experience the emotion of gratitude in between the bowls, the actual process of eating is strictly behavioral. Not automatic, not mechanical, but mindful and yet emotionally neutral. In sum, we could say that Oryoki eating is quintessential un-emotional eating.

Fasting: Wellbeing Through Non-Eating

The East is famous for its fasting. Fasting traditions of the East abound in form and rationale. But what matters in the context of this book and this program is the stark contrast between Western coping by eating and Eastern coping by non-eating. This distinction parallels the Western tendency for changing reality and conquering nature and the Eastern tendency to let reality be as is and to go naturally with the flow. So fasting as a way to feel better or as a coping strategy exists in diametrical opposition to coping through emotional eating. Both clinicians and clients can learn from fasting mentality. An option not to eat does not seem to occur to emotional eaters. And if it does, it does only in the sense of stoic self-denial, only as an abstinence-based attempt "to be good" and avoid emotional eating altogether. As a clinician, you can encourage your clients to look at not-eating as yet another form of coping with an important caveat: "not for the sake of "being good" – that would imply that emotional eating is a bad strategy and it's not - but because non-eating is also a perfectly fine coping strategy that you stand to explore."

Middle Way of Non-Extremes

Jainism predates Buddhism and Buddhism, in a sense, evolved in response to Jainism. Gautauma Buddha, the historical figure who is considered to be the founding mind behind Buddhism, first tried to live the life of a Jain-like ascetic. He joined a band of emaciated ascetics who, not unlike modern-day Jains, roamed the countryside naked in a state of semi-permanent fast. One day, to oversimplify the story, while meditating under a Bodhi tree it dawned on him that the solution to human suffering was in the avoidance of extremes. This realization came to be known as the teaching of the Middle Way. Gautuama decided to give up the life of an itinerant ascetic and rejoined the human tribe. He allowed himself to eat again and in so doing regained some of his physical and social weight. With a fuller stomach he was finally in a position to pass on his teachings about the emptiness of mind.

The point of this apocryphal retelling of Buddha's awakening is to highlight an essential idea for any emotional eater: The way to coping salvation is in non-extremes. Abstinence-based paradigm of "never coping by eating" is a way of self-denial and self-denial is a lousy and extreme platform for long-term change. By the same token, uncontrolled emotional eating that borders on habitual binge-eating (a habit of "always coping by eating") is yet another coping extreme. The path of coping wisdom lies in between these two extremes and it takes the form of occasional emotional eating, particularly, if it is done mindfully. In sum, we could say that mindful emotional eating is a Middle Way emotional eating, which is really just another way of saying that it is a humanistic harm reduction approach.

Enso: Learning from Emptiness

Enso, in Zen Buddhism, is the drawing of a circle. This ritual and, arguably, an art form is a meditation on the void. Enso stands to represent an empty mind of enlightenment in which body is entrusted to just be as it is, to spontaneously go with its own flow, unimpeded by analysis and deliberation. Enso, as I see it, is a meditation on freedom. By now you are probably beginning to see the parallel between enso drawing and my own choice awareness pattern-break of drawing a mindful circle. While the two behaviors are similar in outcome they are quite different in the process. An enso is drawn with an empty mind – no deliberation is involved. A choice-aware circle is drawn with utmost deliberation: You decide where to place the circle, which way to draw it. Yet both drawings carry with them a similarity: an enso circle manifests the inherent spontaneity of the body; a choice aware circle manifests the spontaneity of a pattern-break.

But there is another reason to mention enso in this context. Enso is a meditation on emptiness, on the void that underlies all physical manifestation. But you don't have to be a particle physicist to appreciate this profound philosophical insight. Many an emotional eater is familiar with a feeling of emptiness, a feeling that we rush to pathologize and negate through eating. "Eating fills the void," is what we sometimes hear from our clients. Enso meditation and the concept of void stands to teach us a different way of relating to this curious foundation of reality. Emptiness is its own content, its own fullness, its own substance if you wish. Yes, this sounds esoteric and heady but this idea can be translated into the clinical mechanics of working with emotional eating. As a clinician with one ear open to the Eastern philosophy, ask your emotional eating clients to meditate on this emptiness that they sometimes feel. Ask them to notice it, to go into it, to not fear it, to see that this inner nothingness that sometimes spooks us is too a kind of somethingness.

The idea is to just open up the inquiry: an empty mind, just like an empty stomach, is receptive. Whether we are stuffed with food or certainty, fullness disrupts the connection with the ever-evolving and ever-changing flow of what is. So, fellow clinician and fellow eater, dare to learn from emptiness.

Finding Your Own Grace

East is not the only part of the world that has been historically attuned to the existential majesty and mysticism of eating. Fact is there is no West or East or South or North: a sphere is a sphere. Most of my Western clients are quite familiar with the tradition of Grace – a moment of prayerful mindfulness before the meal. This chapter is in a sense a discussion of Eastern eating grace but the point goes deeper. The mindful emotional eating retraining is a clinical attempt to help your clients find grace in coping through eating. We have been all too unkind to emotional eaters, demonizing emotional eating as some kind of irrational self-destructiveness. But by infusing emotional eating with mindfulness we stand to make coping by eating more graceful, more existentially poignant and more emotionally pragmatic.

Part III: Emotion-Specific MEE

Emotion-specific MEE is for those who have the short-term MEE basics in place. Emotion-specific MEE is advanced MEE as it involves a deeper look into the emotions that we try to palliate with emotional eating. Any time you look deeper into an emotion, it can boomerang. You just might end up feeling even more emotional than you did before. Yet, traditionally, this is where we would begin in therapy: We would ask our clients such questions as "What bothers you?" And we would classically suggest something along the lines: "What if you were to journal about this instead of eating?" We rather recklessly have our clients look into an emotional abyss, without expecting that the abyss would in return look into them. Nietzsche would've wagged his finger at us for such naiveté. In my clinical experience, this has limited therapeutic utility and runs the risk of triggering a bout of uncontrolled emotional eating. Which is why I suggest that you first equip your client with the MEE basics of impulse-control/craving control, bottom-up emotional self-regulation, choice awareness/pattern interruption and lapse/relapse prevention training. And only then offer your client this advanced MEE. Advanced mindful emotional eating is exploratory emotional eating. Put crudely, it's introspection with a pacifier in your mouth. Read on to see what is meant by all of this.

Chapter 16 | Mindful Emotional Eating For Boredom and Emptiness

This is a series of brief emotion-specific chapters about the so-called "big 4" – the big four emotions we try to palliate with emotional eating – boredom, sadness, anger/fear and stress. The last one – stress – is a broad category and it will deal with a gamut of emotional states such as anxiety, overwhelm, and frustration. Notice that we are lumping anger and fear into one emotion, a point that will be explained in a later chapter. We will first tackle boredom and emptiness.

Boredom

Boredom and emptiness sound similar but the two are rather different emotional states. Being able to differentiate between the two helps the intervention. Ask your client if by boredom they mean lack of stimulation, not having much to do, or not knowing how to preoccupy themselves. Boredom, in and of itself, is not necessarily a negative emotional state but a kind of emotional readiness to have some fun, an openness to an enjoyable distraction. If, however, unaddressed boredom quickly morphs into a state of anxious restlessness and angsty frustration.

MEE for Boredom

An abstinence-based perspective is when you are bored you need to find something to do rather than something to eat. A harm-reduction approach takes a different stance here: When bored, eat something, but do so mindfully with the emphasis on tasting rather than eating. Of course, this is not a blanket suggestion for all instances of boredom. It's just a recognition that mindful eating is a legitimate coping option for dealing with boredom. Indeed, food has been and is a source of sensory stimulation. From spices to desserts, tasting, savoring and eating is an entertainment industry in and of itself.

Eating out of boredom is eating for pleasure. Pleasure is an emotion. Thus, eating for pleasure is a form of emotional eating. Therefore, in the spirit of harm reduction, it makes sense to encourage your client to make pleasure-focused eating, which is motivated by boredom, a conscious choice. Unless you and your client are willing to sanction this coping strategy, your client runs the risk of experiencing a guilty pleasure and then coping with this guilt (about an otherwise innocent gustatory indulgence) with mindless "forget it."-style binge eating.

So, the point is quite basic. Tell your client:

"It's okay to eat when you are not hungry but feeling bored and yearning for something pleasurable to do. The idea is not to overdo it. The idea is to indulge on quality not quantity. The idea is focus on tasting and savoring rather than cleaning up your plate. Remember that you are eating for pleasure not because you are hungry. So, it's not about servings but about savoring. Pleasure is an experience. To have it, you have to attend to what you are doing. So, you'll need to kill TV, put your phone away and actually notice what you are putting in your mouth, like you would if you were trying out something new for the first time. And that can be quite stimulating and entertaining and just might help you feel like you are having fun without eating too much."

In sum, the suggestions are as follows:

- When bored, acknowledge that mindful eating is a legitimate coping choice.

- Indulge on quality rather than quantity (after all, you are not really hungry, just hungry for pleasure).

- Focus on savoring rather than on servings.

- Pleasure is an experience; to have pleasure you have to notice what you are tasting, so reduce the distractions (TV, etc.) and notice the food in front of you.

- Make it fun: Try something new.

- Make it social: Go out with company.

- Make it unique: Go out in company to a new place to try out new foods and new settings.

- Try blind-tasting: Buy something new to try and taste it with your eyes closed.

- When bored, go out to a new grocery store or to an ethnic store and get something new to taste.

- When shopping out of boredom, you are shopping for stimulation: Dare to experiment.

- When shopping for stimulation, buy top shelf stuff: Don't skimp out on quality since pleasure is the name of the game here.

- Make it mindful: When eating out of boredom/for pleasure use choice awareness and pattern interruption to keep your mind awake – a mind that is asleep feels no pleasure.

Review these MEE guidelines for boredom and help your client also develop a lapse and relapse prevention plan for making sure that a mindful emotional eating episode for boredom doesn't turn into same old boredom of mindless binge-eating. With this in mind, also help your client to develop a narrative for recovering from a lapse or a relapse. Frame boredom as a learning opportunity with mindful emotional eating being one of the coping options to experiment with.

Emptiness

Feeling "empty" is quite different from feeling bored. A sense of emptiness is a totally different emotional beast than a sense of boredom. But the two have a slight overlapping quality which is why I am talking about them in the same chapter for added juxtaposition. Therefore, mindful emotional eating takes an entirely different course through this emotionally treacherous terrain.

So let us take a reading moment to get a better sense of what this feeling of emptiness really means. Consider the following point: There is really no such thing-less thing as emptiness. The word "emptiness" exists but there is no emptiness. The universe is full; it has no holes. Same goes for "nothingness" – the word exists but what it refers to doesn't. Your client doesn't have to understand this but you do. Helping understand this allows you to set up the following clinical reframe: When your client is feeling "empty" he or she is, in fact, feeling full of something – of something that they don't want to acknowledge, or are afraid to acknowledge. With this in mind, invite your client to open this Pandora's Box. Explain that a feeling of emptiness isn't a state of non-feeling but a feeling of something, of some kind of emotional somethingness. Question is: "*What are you full of when you feel empty?*"

MEE for Emptiness

"What are you full of when you feel empty?" is a tough question. Tough questions scare us particularly when they involve a look inside. Offer your client to use mindful emotional eating as a kind of philosophical pacifier on this journey inside. Help the client see that before they would use food as a kind of gag order for the mind, as a way to shut up that inner voice. Advanced MEE for dealing with emptiness moves you in an entirely different direction – instead of using food to shut up the inner voice, you use food to give that inner voice a safe audience. Think of this as popcorn with a horror movie. Having a little something in your mouth allows you to keep just enough distance from the horror on the mind/screen. More specifically, invite your client to "go into this emptiness" so as "to see what it is about." And explain: "You don't have to go into this abyss of emptiness without props. Make some popcorn or get a handful of raisins and make this journey a bit sweeter, a bit lighter."

For some clients this is all the direction that they need. Others crave more structure. So, here's a protocol of sorts:

- Get a handful of raisins.

- Sit down, close your eyes and relax with a few humful breaths.

- Now put a raisin in your mouth and mindfully eat it: taste it, chew it, savor it, swallow it.

- Now, get on the riverbank of your mind and ask yourself a question: "What am I empty of?"

- Notice the thoughts that pop into your mind: Let them come to let them go, refocusing on your breath in between thoughts.

- Now put another raisin in your mouth and mindfully eat it.

- Now get back on the riverbank of your mind and repeat the question: "What am I still empty of? What is amiss right now?"

- Notice the thoughts that pop into your mind: Let them come to let them go, refocusing on your breath in between thoughts.

- Repeat as needed.

- Finish with another course of relaxation: Take a few humful breaths.

- Open your eyes and journal about what you have learned from this feeling of "emptiness" if you please.

Walk your client through this protocol in session, if you feel it'll help. Encourage your client to experiment with this meditation on emptiness. Process the insights at the follow-up session.

No Need to Fear Emotions or Emotional Eating

The overarching point here is to help your client not to fear emotions or emotional eating as a way of coping with emotions. Mindful emotional eating is a legitimate coping inquiry into self. By clinically endorsing this kind of mindful emotional eating you are helping your client broaden their crisis coping repertoire. Boredom and emptiness can be very destabilizing. Knowing that mindful emotional eating is an option makes all the difference between effective and ineffective coping.

Chapter 17 | Mindful Emotional Eating for Sadness and Grief

Sadness and grief come with voracious appetite. When down or alone, when betrayed or disappointed, when abandoned or bereaved, we seek the original comfort of the womb and eating is our closest approximation of that. The adults that we are, we don't want to suck our thumbs – seems too embarrassing, too regressive. So, we escape into unmediated oral coping – we fill up on the familiar comforts of existence, on the one and only aspect of reality that we can depend on –food. Food doesn't betray. Food doesn't abandon. Food never fails.

Sadness, Grief, Loss

All sadness is grief and all grief is sadness. Both sadness and grief are reactions to loss – a loss of spouse, a loss of job, a loss of self-view. This loss-based kind of suffering is inevitable and is grounded in our barnacle-like attachment to fleeting circumstance. No, we are not silly to attach, we are not stupid to cling, we are not short-sighted to get used to that which is fleeting – we are simply courageous to take a risk of insisting on how reality should be. We dare to dream, to fantasize, to plan. But we are all married to reality and reality is an unfaithful partner. Reality makes no promises, it owes nothing to anyone, it is its own thing-less thing, ever morphing, ever changing, ever minding its own business and never minding the collateral damage of our emotions. Reality, like a finicky lover, is constantly breaking up with us. We thought it was going to be "this" but – bam! – it became "that." We readjusted but "that" changed back into "this" or became an altogether different kind of "X." We are partnered with the bewildering unknown, and we constantly have to mourn the loss of illusory certainty that we tried to plan our lives around.

Impermanence

All plans, all expectations are just writings on water and it takes us a very long time to get this. Each time we experience sadness, we grieve the loss of some vision, of some certainty, of some peace of mind. And each time we stand to either learn or not about the fundamental condition of reality which is impermanence. Heraclitus, a Greco-Buddhist, once said, "you can't enter the same river twice." Buddhist themselves speak of anitya – the impermanence of reality. Understanding that everything passes, that you cannot hold on to anything, that life isn't fixed is a bitter-sweet insight; it's a loss of control and a gain of serenity. And mindful eating can be a handy intro into this insight.

MEE: Existentially Poignant Eating

Process-focused mindful eating is inadvertently a meditation on impermanence. You take a bite – here it is, this food in your mouth. And now it's gone. You take another bite – same ending. An empty pint of ice cream was just full, full of promise, full of potential pleasure, full of coping calories. But now it's empty while you fiddle with a TV remote in your hand, surfing the waves of electronic impermanence to anchor your mind in something that holds your interest.

Mindless emotional eating, in my opinion, only deepens sadness and grief. In its futility to teach you something, in its largely unsatisfying tendency to mindlessly fleet by, it seems to only underscore our struggle with impermanence. In contrast, mindful emotional eating helps us accept the inevitable flow of change.

So, if you or your client has some sadness or grief to mindlessly eat away, offer them a choice of working through this sadness and grief with the help of mindful emotional eating. How? Well, here's a possible behavioral-meditative sequence to try. Call it "cathartic eating."

- Choose to eat mindfully to cope with sadness, grief and loss.
- Have a few humful breaths as the first course of this mindful emotional eating episode.
- Wake up your mind – take it off the autopilot (with choice awareness and pattern interruption).
- Set some food in front of you and take a look at it. Recognize the existential metaphor of this:

*Here is, in front of me, a potential for a moment of satisfaction
and happiness, an opportunity to feel good, to feel comforted,
to feel in control. I know all there is to know about this next
moment: I will eat, I know how to eat, I know what that will
be like – this food will please me somewhat. But I also know
that this food will not last. This moment, this meal, this attempt
at coping, this experience of satisfaction and certainty that comes
with doing something familiar will too pass. And in this I dare
to recognize the law of reality: everything passes. But this time
I acknowledge this as inevitable and therefore normal.
And I choose not to fear this impermanence.*

• Having opened up to this inevitable impermanence of the
moment, proceed with it: Eat what's in front of you and, if you
feel like it, cry through this. Allow yourself to mourn the futility
of holding on to pleasure, the futility of holding on to meaning,
the futility of holding on to circumstance. All passes. All will pass.
And so will your sadness and grief about whatever it is that you
are mourning today.

• Finish the way you started with a few humful breaths.

• Congratulate yourself on trying to make peace with
impermanence with the help of mindful, existentially-poignant,
emotional eating.

Eating With Courage

As you see, this kind of cathartic emotional eating is eating with courage,
with courage to be, with courage to be in the now with what is. And that is
quintessential mindfulness. This kind of emotional eating doesn't run from
sadness or grief, it runs towards it. This kind of emotional eating doesn't run
from reality, it faces it. This kind of emotional eating doesn't run from one's
feelings, it faces them. With courage, with tears, with presence.

Chapter 18 | Mindful Emotional Eating for Anger and Fear

This isn't going to be very easy but what is, right? So, I might as well get going with this. So, here's my thesis: Anger and fear are two sides of one and the same evolutionary coin. You've heard it put differently: "A good offence is the best defense." But that's sports commentators for you. Here's an anger management expert for you, Ron Potter-Efron: "In terms of many threatening situations it may be wise to think of anger and fear as one combined emotional reaction" (2012, p. 46). Hopefully, it is clinically clear to you that anger, in most of its manifestations, is a self-defensive reaction. Which is why we choose to lump fear and anger together into this chapter on how to use advanced mindful emotional eating to deal with these two. Correction: How to deal with this one two-sided emotional coin.

The Zero-Sum of Life

Life is zero-sum. Meaning: To eat we have to kill. Whether we eat a bucket of chicken wings or a bowl of organically grown pea soup from your local co-op, we consume life. Sure, a peapod doesn't quack like a peacock, but life is life. Neither fauna nor flora wants to die. Just because a stalk of wheat isn't on Facebook® it doesn't mean that it isn't alive. Point, once again, is unless you subsist on packets of NutraSweet®, the sweetness of your eating life is built on the bitterness of death. We kill to live. And this is normal. We are just numb to it unless we stumble upon a heart-wrenching video of an emaciated cow being bullied with a forklift. So, we turn a blind eye. Or become vegetarian, or vegan. But that's still blindness. Anything that's alive wants to live. No life-form, no matter how primitive, is indifferent to its own survival.

So, where are we going with this reality check? To this realization: Violence is normal and as hard as we can try to minimize it, at the end of it all, we still have to conclude that the business of living is an unfair business, a painful business, somebody somewhere is always getting hurt. And today this might happen to be you: somebody said something to upset you, somebody keyed your car, somebody got you fired, somebody cut in front of you in the check-out aisle, somebody somewhere stepped on your toes. That is life. Normal life. Painful but normal life. And when I say this I don't mean to minimize your suffering or invalidate it. On the contrary, I am taking time to acknowledge it and inviting you to consider a different way of acknowledging it yourself – with the help of mindful emotional eating.

MEE: Eating Justice

The abstinence-based approach to emotional eating is a non-approach. You are not allowed to approach emotions – such as fear and anger – through eating. You are told to avoid emotional eating at all costs. And that, of course, only upsets you more. And only scares you even more: If you can't eat to cope with your anger and fear, then what are your options? Well, the options, as you would be advised by an abstinence-focused clinician, are to not eat to cope and to cope by not eating.

What about a harm reduction take on this issue? You've probably guessed by now: yes, you can eat to cope with fear and anger, as long as you are willing to try to do it mindfully. Furthermore, I'd like to suggest a particular kind of mindful emotional eating angle that can help you make peace with this dog-eat-dog world that angers and scares you. Here's how this line of thinking goes:

- When angry or afraid, choose to cope with these emotions through mindful eating.

- Get a burger (even if you are a vegan or a vegetarian) or a chicken sandwich or a fish filet, fry yourself some bacon.

- And as you bite into it, meditate on the normal injustice of eating:

"This cow had to die by electrocution or some other gruesome means, this fish had to end its life in a bucket of water with a hook in its mouth or suffocate in a net on the bottom of some fishing boat… And yet you do have to eat. You too deserve to enjoy yourself while you are alive. This cow or this fish or this chicken or this pig didn't think twice about what life they grazed on or consumed, what bugs they stepped on while grazing or swallowed inadvertently. These animals didn't give a hoot as to whether the grass hurts when mowed down. And, yes, yes, you are a clever little monkey, you have a big brain, so you ought to know better, you say to yourself.

Well, now is exactly the time for you to know better… this very moment of eating is a moment of eating justice… but also a moment of forgiveness. Life lives. Life does what it needs to do to live another day. Sometimes mindlessly, sometimes mindfully. Life is self-serving, invariably selfish and all of this is normal. And just like you didn't really mean to hurt anyone when you bit into this burger, the person that stepped on your toes, that upset you, that scared you – at the end of the day, at the bottom of analysis – didn't do it to hurt you but did it to doggedly pursue their own wellbeing. Sure, he or she might have purposefully set up to lose a job so that they can take your spot under the sun. But it wasn't personal. It was about them, about their own pursuit of wellbeing. So, as you mindfully chew on this once-vibrant living flesh, forgive yourself and forgive whoever you need to forgive and, if you dare, make peace with this dog-eat-dog, human-beat-human world. Recognize that life is zero-sum. It has to be. This is neither good nor bad. It just is. And hopefully, with this realization you can finally enjoy your own eating moment under this sun."

A Bite of Self-Forgiveness

As you can see, fellow clinician and fellow eater, mindful eating is existentially sobering: It teaches us about the fundamental selfishness of living and in so doing it allows us to make peace with that which is fundamental has to be acknowledged as normal. Mindful eating of the kind that is proposed here is *emotional* eating, it begins with guilt but works its way to self-forgiveness and from there it is only a hop and a skip to fearlessly forgiving others. Help your client see how this kind of contemplative emotional eating can, in fact, help us begin to make peace with the jungle of existence.

Chapter 19 | Mindful Emotional Eating for Stress

Stress eating is as common as stress. Stress eating is quintessential emotional eating. In fact, these two phrases frequently mean the exact same thing. But this isn't an empty distinction. Emotional eating can be celebratory, it can be out of boredom, it can be ritualistic and not necessarily palliative in its intention. So, it helps not to lump stress eating and emotional eating together. Emotional eating is a larger category, it's an overarching rubric, with stress eating being a big palliative branch of it. But the topic of stress eating is hardly new, so I'll be brief and to the point.

Parasympathetic Self-Regulation

Eating turns on the relaxation response (this was briefly discussed earlier in the book when making a case for emotional eating in contrast with the usual case against it). Eating when stressed is an intuitive coping shortcut. What we want to emphasize to our clients here is the idea of effectiveness. If you or your client wants to cope with stress by eating then, of course, they can, particularly if they have a plan in mind for how to leverage maximum coping per calorie. So, this is where you would review the MEE basics – such as "first course of relaxation," humful breathing to leverage NO and other parasympathetic self-regulation tricks of the trade. But there is more to it and that's what this brief chapter is about.

Slow Emotional Eating

Slow eating is when you try to eat slowly. Slow eating is a form of mindful eating. It is relaxing, it is self-soothing, it is self-indulgent. You take your time. You put the utensils down in between the bites. You look around and sip wine as you go. You enjoy a good view and good company.

Slow emotional eating, to coin a term, is when you make a conscious choice to eat to cope and you incorporate the slow-eating-know-how.

Typically, stress eating is rushed. You feel like you can't wait to relax so you inhale whatever is in front of you and then you are done. But you don't feel done – you ate too fast. Maybe you feel a little better, but you want more time with this pacifier. And that's where slow eating naturally comes in. The following is a list of slow emotional eating suggestions to leverage the most coping per calorie:

- Give yourself the permission to cope by eating.

- Start with a few humful breaths as the first course.

- Allow yourself to indulge on quality not quantity: Eat only what you want to eat, no point in compromising a moment of self-indulgence.

- Take your time: Set an alarm clock for at least ten or twenty minutes and claim this entire eating time as yours.

- If possible, get some company (but agree to focus on food and not turn this slow emotional eating into a therapy session).

- If possible, find a place with a view: If necessary, bundle up so that you can sit on outside or just drag your chair up to the window.

- If you drink in moderation, pour yourself half a glass of wine.

- Use some choice awareness or pattern interruption tricks to keep your mind awake: Try a non-dominant hand or wrong or unfamiliar utensils to slow down the hand-to-mouth mechanics.

- Make a point to put down the utensils.

- Make your point to catch your breath in between the mouthfuls and mindfuls.

- Take a few moments to deconstruct your eating into tasting, savoring and actual eating (*see Eating the Moment*, Somov 2008 for details).

- Give yourself the permission not to finish anything, you don't have to clean your plate.

- If you want a dessert, have a dessert but do finish with the dessert of relaxation, have yourself a few humful breaths before you get up from the table.

From Stress Eating to Stress Management Eating

At the risk for stating the obvious, let me highlight an important point. Stress eating is stressful. Stress eating, or classic emotional eating, is rushed. As such, it creates stress – you eat to de-stress but you end up stressing out about how much you just mindlessly ate. Help your client see this ineffectiveness and help them make a semantic shift from ineffective stress eating to effective stress management eating. How? Once again, by taking their time to eat slowly, to cope mindfully, i.e. to manage their stress effectively.

Take the Words Out of the Client's Mouth

Recognize that slow eating is invariably emotional eating. The very point behind slow eating is not to eat or to aid digestion but to relax. Slow eating is relaxed eating. So, once again we are talking emotional eating. Thus, slow emotional eating is relaxed emotional eating and as such a perfect anti-dote to stress eating. As a clinician, I often find myself working hard to help my clients collapse false semantic dualities. What I just said in the two or three sentences above is an example of how by continuously reframing the issue we stand to purify it of its self-invalidating connotations. Ask any client if they oppose slow eating and the answer is "of course not." Ask them if they oppose stress eating and the answer is likely to be "yes." Yet, stress eating in its mandate is indistinguishable from slow eating. Both aim at relaxation. So my suggestion to you, fellow clinician, dare to mince words – dare to engage your client in a brief Socratic dialogue of what all this horrible stress eating or emotional eating is meant to accomplish and help your client arrive at a position of self-acceptance. Collapse the toxic semantic dualities that stem from abstinence-focused thinking to give your client a face-saving go-ahead to cope by eating with more effectiveness and self-compassion.

References

Amen, D. (1998). *Change Your Brain, Change Your Life: The Breakthrough Program for Conquering Anxiety, Depression, Obsessiveness, Anger and Impulsiveness.* Three Rivers Press, NY.

Baumeister, R. & Tierney, J. (2012). *Willpower: Rediscovering the Greatest Human Strength.* Penguin Books

Benson, H. & Proctor, W. (2010) *Relaxation Revolution: Enhancing Your Personal Health Through the Science and Genetics of Mind-Body Healing.* New York: Scribner.

Bryan, N. S., & Zand, J., with Gottlieb, B. (2010). *The Nitric Oxide (NO) Solution: How to Boost the Body's Miracle Molecule to Prevent and Reverse Chronic Disease.* Austin, TX: Neogenis

Campbell, D. (2001). The Mozart Effect: *Tapping the Power of Music to Heal the Body, Strengthen the Mind, and Unlock the Creative Sp*irit. Quill

Craighead, L. (2006). *The Appetite Awareness Workbook: How to Listen to Your Body and Overcome Bingeing, Overeating, and Obsession with Food.* New Harbinger Publications. Oakland, CA.

Davy, B. M., Dennis, E. A., Dengo, A. L., & Davy, K. P. (2008). *Water Consumption Reduces Energy Intake at a Breakfast Meal in Obese Older Adults.* Journal of the American Dietetic Association 108 (7): 1236-1239.

Delaney, B. & Walford, L. (2010). *The Longevity Diet: the Only Proven Way to Slow the Aging Process and Maintain Peak Vitality-Through Caloric Restriction.* DaCapo Press

Hanson, R. (2009). *Buddha's Brain: The Practical Neuroscience of Happiness, Love, and Wisdom.* With R. Mendius. Oakland, CA: New Harbinger Publications.

Somov, P. (2008). *Eating the Moment:* 141 Mindful Practices for Overcoming One Meal at a Time. Oakland, CA: New Harbinger Publications

Somov, P. (2012). *Reinventing the Meal: How Mindfulness Can Help You Slow Down, Savor the Moment & Reconnect With the Ritual of Eating.* Oakland, CA: New Harbinger Publications

Somov, P. & Somova, M. (2003). *Recovery Equation: Motivational Enhancement, Choice Awareness, Use Prevention: An Innovative Clinical Curriculum for Substance Use Treatment.* New York: Imprint Books.

Weitzberg, E. & Lundberg, J. O. (2002). Humming Greatly Increases Nasal Nitric Oxide. *American Journal of Respiratory and Critical Care Medicine, 166* (2):144-145.